MENSA BRAIN TWISTERS

Helene Hovanec, Karen C. Richards
& Martin Gardner

**OFFICIAL MENSA
PUZZLE BOOK**

Main Street
A division of Sterling Publishing Co., Inc.
New York

2 4 6 8 10 9 7 5 3 1

This collection is excerpted from the following Sterling titles:
Mental Magic © 1999 by Martin Gardner
Illustrations by Jeff Sinclair
Brainteasers for Young Einsteins © 2001 by Helene Hovanec
Mighty Mini Mind Bogglers © 1999 by Karen C. Richards

Published by Sterling Publishing Co., Inc.
387 Park Avenue South, New York, NY 10016
© 2004 by Sterling Publishing Co., Inc.
Distributed in Canada by Sterling Publishing

C/o Canadian Manda Group, One Atlantic Avenue, Suite 105
Toronto, Ontario, Canada M6K 3E7
Distributed in Great Britain and Europe by Chris Lloyd at Orca Book
Services, Stanley House, Fleets Lane, Poole BH15 3AJ, England
Distributed in Australia by Capricorn Link (Australia) Pty. Ltd.
P.O. Box 704, Windsor, NSW 2756, Australia

Printed in United States of America
All rights reserved

ISBN 1-4027-1641-9

CONTENTS

MENTAL MAGIC

INTRODUCTION

Professor Picanumba, who for many years lived alone in a cave near the top of a distant high mountain, has developed the incredible ability to predict what you will do. Here in this section, our esteemed professor presents a series of tests in which you are asked to freely select certain numbers, words, or pictures. In the back of the section, the professor, having accessed his great power of precognition, has had printed there the outcome of each exercise—before you've even done it!

Work your way carefully through each test, doing just what the professor has asked you to do. When you arrive at the final outcome, turn to the page at the back of this section, labeled "The Professor Predicts," for his prediction under the name of the exercise. You'll be amazed by how accurate the old fellow is!

Almost every time, the professor will predict exactly the final result of each test. On a couple of occasions he has made a guess that may or may not be correct, but most of the time his guesses will be right on the mark.

Before starting these tests, you should have on hand a deck of cards, four dice, a calculator, a pencil and a supply of paper. A few puzzles require using other items, but they are usually available around the home.

The word "digit," used throughout the section, means one of the numerals 0, 1, 2, 3, 4, 5, 6, 7, 8 and 9.

Martin Gardner, D.F.
(Doctor of Flimflam)

WONDERLAND SPELL

Here is how Lewis Carroll began *Alice in Wonderland:*

> Alice was beginning to get very tired of sitting by her sister on the bank, and of having nothing to do: once or twice she had peeped into the book her sister was reading.

Select any of the first 12 words. Starting on the next word, spell the word you chose, tapping a word for each letter. For example, if you selected the word "Alice" you spell A-L-I-C-E. Counting words for letters, this takes you to the word "very." So you spell V-E-R-Y, next ending on "by." Keep going. Note the word on which your spelling chain ends. What's the word?

Answer on page 114.

A MYSTERIOUS MATRIX

Make a copy of the 6-by-6 matrix on the next page.

Circle any number, then cross out all the numbers in the same row and the same column as the number you circled.

28	26	30	27	29	25
34	32	36	33	35	31
16	14	18	15	17	13
4	2	6	3	5	1
10	8	12	9	11	7
22	20	24	21	23	19

Select any number *not* crossed out and circle it.
Again, cross out all numbers in the same row and same
column as the circled number.

Repeat this four more times. There will be six circled
numbers, each randomly chosen.

Add the six numbers. What's the total?

Answer on page 106.

CARDS THAT SHAKE DICE

In this exercise you use a deck of cards to simulate the
tossing of a pair of dice.

Shuffle the cards, then start dealing them face up to
form pile A. Stop as soon as a card turns up with a
value of 1 through 6. This number represents the toss
of one die.

As soon as you get a die number on pile A, start
dealing a new pile, B. Again, stop as soon as a card
appears with a value of 1 through 6. This represents
the toss of another die. Add the two numbers, and
write the sum on a sheet of paper. The sum is as
randomly obtained as if you had tossed a pair of dice.

After recording the results of the first "throw" of imaginary dice, shove the two piles aside and repeat the dealing into two more piles, to obtain a second dice "throw." Write the results of this second "throw" below the previous number.

Continue making "throws" in this manner until the entire deck has been used. Add all the "throws." Because each "throw" was as random as a toss of two dice, it seems impossible that Professor Picanumba could predict the sum of all the "throws."

What's the final sum?

Answer on page 99.

TRY THIS ON A DOLLAR BILL

Write down the serial number from any dollar bill. Scramble the digits any way you like—that is, mix up their order. Jot down this second number.

Using your calculator, subtract the smaller number from the larger.

From the difference, take 7.

Copy the digits now on display, then add them all together. If the sum is more than one digit, add the digits once more. Keep adding the digits in the sums until just one digit is obtained.

What is it?

Answer on page 112.

THE MAGIC OF 8

Multiply your phone number (disregard its area code) by 8. Write down the following three numbers:

1. Your phone number.
2. 8.
3. The product of your phone number and 8.

214   6025
8
1768200

Add all the digits in those three numbers. If the sum is more than one digit, add again. Continue in this way until a single digit is reached.

What's the digit?

Answer on page 105.

AROUND THE SQUARE

Toss a die on the table. Enter the number it shows into your calculator.

Multiply the number by 8.

Add 4.

Add the number on top of the die.

32
4
36
40

Now, on the grid at the left, put your finger on cell A and say "One." Tap clockwise around the square, tapping the cells as you go, and counting, "two, three, four," and so on. Stop tapping when you reach the number on your calculator's display.

On what letter did your finger end the count?

Answer on page 99.

NATION, ANIMALS, FRUIT

Write down the following words:

1. The name of a nation that begins with D.

Domanican rebullic

2. An animal that begins with the second letter of the
   nation.   *Ostrich*
3. The color of the animal.
   pink
4. An animal that begins with the *last* letter of the
   nation.   *kangaroo*
5. A fruit that begins with the last letter of the animal
   selected in step 4.   *orange*

As a bonus, Professor Picanumba will tell you where
you got those shoes you are wearing.

Answers on page 106.

THE RED AND THE BLACK

Shuffle a deck of cards, then deal 30 cards to the table
to form a pile.

Count the number of black cards in the pile. From
this number, subtract the number of red cards in the
rest of the deck. What's the difference?

Here's a quick question. If you add up all the
digits in 1234567890 the sum is 45. If instead you

multiply all the digits, will the product be more or less than 100?

Answers on page 107.

THE EXACT WORD

Think of any word on this page. Concentrate on it, then turn to the answer section. Believe it or not, the answer will print the exact word!

Answer on page 101.

A TWO-DICE TEST

Toss a die. Think of a number from 1 through 6. Put another die on top of the one you tossed, turning it so the number you thought of is on top of the stack.

Carefully check the numbers on the two faces of the dice that are touching. Add those two numbers to the number you thought of, and write it down.

Think of another number from 1 through 6. Add it to the last result.

Remove the top die of the stack. Turn it so your second selected number is on top. Remove it from the stack and place it alongside the other die.

Lift up both dice. Add the sum of their *bottom* faces to your previous total.

What's your final sum?

Answer on page 112.

A CURIOUS COUNT

Shuffle a deck of cards, then start dealing them face up to form a pile. Say "Ten" when you deal the first card, "Nine" when you deal the second, "Eight" when you deal the third, and so on. In other words, as you deal you count backward from ten to one.

Assume that each face card (king, queen, or jack) has a value of 10.

As soon as you deal a card with a value that is the same as the number you say aloud, stop dealing and start a new pile. If you reach one without finding a

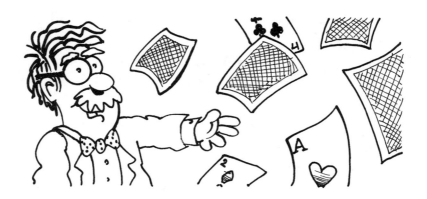

match, "kill" the pile by putting a card face down on top of it.

Repeat this procedure until you have dealt four piles. If all four have been "killed," which is very unlikely, start the test all over again after another shuffle of the deck.

After the four piles are finished, add the values of the cards at the top of each "living" pile. Call this sum "k".

Deal "k" cards from the remainder of the deck, then count the cards that remain.

How many are they?

Answer on page 100.

A ROTATING MATRIX

Think of a number from 1 through 16. Locate that number on the border of the matrix below. Turn the page so the number is at the top of the matrix. 14

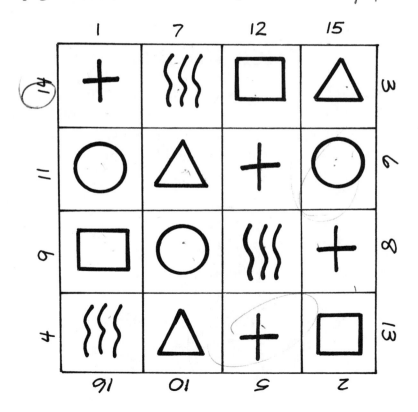

Count out that number of cells from left to right, top to bottom, starting the count on the top left corner cell. Note the symbol in the cell where the count ends.
What symbol is it?

Answer on page 108.

CATCH THE BILL

Hold a dollar bill by one end as shown. Position your right hand so your thumb is on one side, fingers on the other, as if you are about to catch the bill when your left hand drops it. Your thumb and fingers must not touch the bill.

Let go with your left hand, and you will find that it is very easy to catch the bill in the other hand before it falls to the floor.

Now let someone else hold the bill while you try to catch it after it is dropped.

Can you catch the bill before it falls?

Answer on page 100.

FIVE IN A ROW

Remove from a deck the nine of diamonds, the four of hearts, the queen of hearts, the ace of diamonds, and the seven of clubs.

Place the five cards face up in a row in the order shown here.

As you can see, there is one picture card, one ace, and one black card. Look them over carefully. Select one of the five cards and write it down.

Your choice is entirely free. What card did you write down?

Answer on page 102.

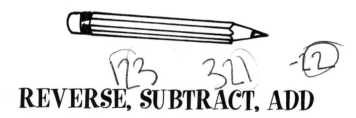

REVERSE, SUBTRACT, ADD

Write down any three-digit number, provided no zero is used and the first and last digits differ by more than 1.

Reverse the three digits to make a second number. For example, if you thought of 387 the reverse number would be 783.

Subtract the smaller number of the two from the larger. Reverse the result, then add it to the subtraction result.

926
629

Now translate the sum into a word by using the following chart:

S	M	A	R	T
1	2	3	4	5
6	7	8	9	0

For each digit in the sum, substitute the letter at the top of the column. What word do you get?

Answer on page 108.

A GEOMETRY TEST

Draw a simple geometrical figure. Inside it, draw another simple geometric figure.
What did you draw?

Answer on page 103.

MONKEY BUSINESS

If you had ten bananas and a monkey stole all but six how many bananas would you have left?

Answer on page 105

FACE-UP CARDS

Divide a deck into two halves of 26 cards each. Turn one half over so all its cards are face up. Shuffle them into the other half, which remains face down. Keep shuffling as long as you like, until you are satisfied the cards are thoroughly mixed.

Deal 26 cards to the table to form a pile. Put the rest of the deck down to make a second pile. Turn over either pile.

Count the number of face-up cards in each pile. What is the difference between the two counts?

Answer on page 101

WHAT'S ON THE PAPER?

Write any word you like on a sheet of paper. Fold the paper twice, then put it down and stand on it. Believe it or not, Professor Picanumba will tell you what is on the paper!

In addition, the professor will explain a method that enables you to see right through the walls of a house!

Answers on page 113.

COUNT THE CLIPS

Remove the contents of a small box of paper clips. Place exactly 20 clips in the box and set the rest of them aside.

Select a number fewer than ten. Take that number of clips out of the box and put them in your pocket.

Count the number of clips remaining in the box. Add the two digits of the count and remove that number of paper clips from the box. Put them in your pocket.

Take out three more paper clips.
How many clips are left in the box?

Answer on page 100.

NUMBER, FLOWER, COLOR

Think of a number between 10 and 50 that consists of
two different digits, both of them odd. The numbers
11 and 33 are ruled out because their digits are alike.
Write down the number you selected.

Under the number write the name of a flower.

Under the flower write a color. Most people think
first of red, so *don't* pick red.

What are your three choices?

Answers on page 106.

IN PRAISE OF RED

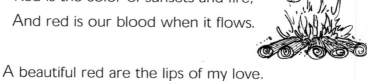

Red is the color of sunsets and fire,
And red is our blood when it flows.

A beautiful red are the lips of my love.
They rival the red of a rose.

We thrill to the red of a cardinal's wings,
But not to a sunburned red nose!

* * *

Roll one of your dice on the table. Let "n" be
the number it shows. Look at the "n"th line
of the poem above. Count to the "n"th
word of that "n"th line.
What is the word?

red

Answer on page 104.

THREE HEAPS

Form three heaps of paper clips in a row on the table. Each heap must contain the same number of clips, and there must be more than three clips in each heap. (If paper clips are not handy, you can use beans, raisins, matchsticks, toothpicks, or any other set of small objects.)

Take three clips from each end heap and put them on the middle heap. Count the number of clips in

either end heap. Remove that number of clips from the center heap and place them on one of the end heaps.

Take a single clip from either end heap and put it in the middle heap.

How many clips are now in the middle heap?

Answer on page 111.

FOLD AND TRIM

Fold a sheet of paper in half four times, then unfold it. The creases will form a 4-by-4 matrix of cells as shown below.

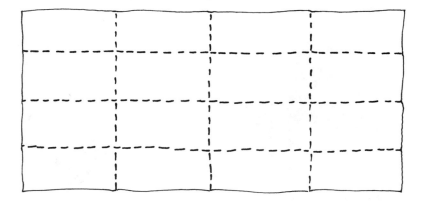

Number the cells from 1 through 16 as shown below. Fold each crease forward and back a few times so the paper will fold easily either way along each crease.

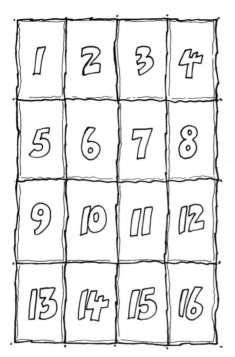

Now fold the sheet into a packet the size of one cell. You can make the folds as tricky as you please, folding this way, that way—any way you like. You may even tuck folds between folds. In other words, make the folding as random as possible

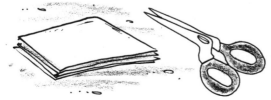

until you have a packet the size of a single cell.

With the scissors, trim away all four edges of the folded paper packet so that it consists of sixteen separate pieces. Spread the pieces on the table. Some pieces will have their number-side up, others their number-side down.

Add all the numbers on the face-up pieces. What is the sum?

Answer on page 102.

NUMBER NAMES

Think of any number from 1 through 100. Write down its name.

Count the number of letters in its name to obtain a second number.

Count the number of letters in the second number to obtain a third number.

Continue in this way until the chain of numbers ends on a number that keeps repeating.

What is this number?

Answer on page 106.

A TEST WITH TWO DICE

Roll a pair of dice on the table. Call them A and B. Write down the following four different products:

1. The product of the top numbers on the dice.

2. The product of their bottom numbers.

3. The product of the top of A and the bottom of B.

4. The product of the top of B and the bottom of A.

Add the four products.

What is the sum?

Answer on page 110.

THINK-A-LETTER

Select any one of the twenty-six letters of the alphabet. Look for your thought-of letter in each of the five columns on the next page. Write down the letter at the top of each column in which your selected letter appears.

Change these letters to numbers, using the code A = 1, B = 2, C = 3, D = 4, and so on. Add the numbers that you obtain in this way.

Using the same code, turn the sum you get back into a letter. What letter does it yield?

A	**B**	**D**	**H**	**P**
C	C	E	I	Q
E	F	F	J	R
G	G	G	K	S
I	J	L	L	T
K	K	M	M	U
M	N	N	N	V
O	O	O	O	W
Q	R	T	X	X
S	S	U	Y	Y
U	V	V	Z	Z
W	W	W	Y	Z

Answer on page 111.

TURN TWO AND CUT

Hold a packet of ten cards face down in your left hand. Turn the top pair of cards face up, then cut the packet at any spot you like. Again, turn the top two cards face up and cut. Keep up this turning a pair and cutting for as long as you like. This, of course, will randomize the positions of the face-up cards in the packet.

After you decide to stop reversing and cutting, deal the cards in a row on the table. Reverse all the cards at even positions along the row; that is, turn over the second, fourth, sixth, eighth, and tenth card.

How many cards in the row will now be face up?

Answer on page 112.

THE ROTATED DIE

Place a die on the square shape on the next page so that you can see its 1, 2, and 3 faces, as shown to the right of the square.

Give the die a quarter turn in any of two ways. You may rotate it clockwise or the other way, keeping it on the square, or you can tip it over an edge in any of the

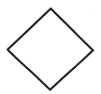 

four directions, then slide it back onto the square. Each turn replaces one of the three visible faces by another face.

After you have made 13 random turns, add the three faces you now see. Is the sum odd or even?

Answer on page 108.

AN ABCABC NUMBER

Think of any three-digit number ABC. Enter it twice into your calculator as a six-digit number ABCABC.

Seven and 11 are lucky dice numbers, and 13 is considered an unlucky number.

Divide ABCABC by 7. Professor Picanumba predicts there will be no remainder. Sure enough, he's right!

Divide the result now on display by 11. The Professor again predicts correctly that there is no remainder.

Finally, divide the number on display by 13. Once more, there is no remainder.

What number is now showing on your calculator?

Answer on page 98.

A DOMINO CHAIN

You need a complete set of 28 dominoes to do this test. Remove the one domino that has 2 and 5 spots. Put it in your pocket.

Now pretend that you are playing a solitaire game of dominoes. Form the 27 pieces into one long single chain, placing them any way you like. When completed, note the number of spots at each end of the chain.

What are those two numbers?

Answer on page 100.

THE GRY TEST

Think of a word that ends in GRY.

Professor Picanumba will tell you the word that you thought of. As a bonus, he'll tell you within four days the day you were born!

Now, how about a little riddle? A cowboy rode into Bottleneck on Friday, stayed three days, then rode out of town on Friday. How come?

Answers on page 103.

WHISK THE DIME

Hold your left hand palm up and put a dime on the center of the palm.

With a whisk broom in your other hand, try to

brush the dime off your left hand.

Can you do it?

Here's another riddle. A barber in Chicago says he'd rather cut the hair of ten red-headed men than the hair of one brown-haired man. Can you guess why?

Answers on page 114.

BEAST, CITY, VEGETABLE

Write down words for the following:

1. A wild beast.

2. The largest city of a foreign country.

3. A vegetable.

What are the three words?

Answers on page 99.

A TEST WITH YOUR AGE

Enter your age in the calculator.

Multiply it by 12.

Add the mysterious number 2856.

Divide by 3.

Divide by 4.

Subtract your age.

What number is now on display?

Answer on page 110.

A SURPRISING SUM

On the opposite page are four circles. Copy them on a sheet of paper.

Choose any number in Circle 1. Cross it out, then write it down as the first digit of a number that you

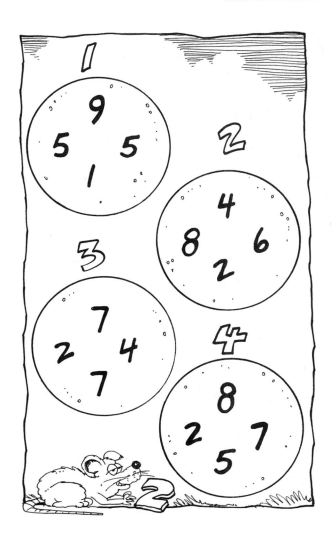

are creating.

Select any digit in Circle 2. Cross it out. Put it down as the second digit of the number you are forming.

Select a digit in Circle 3. Cross it out and make it the third digit of your number.

Select a digit in Circle 4. Cross it out. This will be the fourth and last digit of your number.

Now create three more four-digit numbers in exactly the same way. Select the digits from the four circles, taking the circles in numerical order. Cross out digits as you use them.

You now have randomly formed four numbers, each with four digits. Add the four random numbers.

What's the total?

Answer on page 110.

AROUND THE SOLAR SYSTEM

For this test you need a dime and eight pennies.

Place a dime on any of the nine cells shown on the opposite page.

Spell the name on that cell by moving the dime one

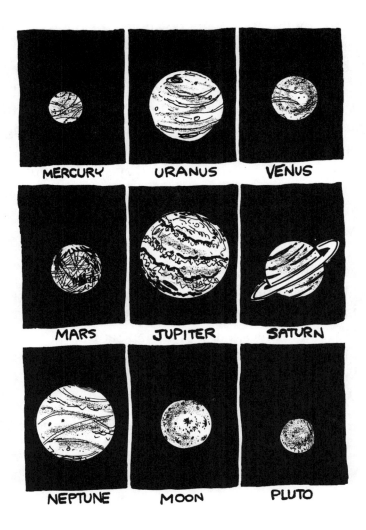

step in any direction—up, down, left, or right—to an adjacent square. Diagonal moves are not permitted. At each move spell a letter. For example, if you put the dime on Mars, spell M-A-R-S by moving the dime in any of the possible directions, one move for each letter. You can imagine that the dime is a spaceship moving around the solar system.

After you have moved the dime by spelling, put a penny on Venus. From now on you must not move the dime to a cell occupied by a penny.

Move the dime seven times, then put a penny on Mars.

Move three times. Put a penny on Mercury.

Move seven times. Put a penny on Uranus.

Move five times. Put a penny on Neptune.

Move nine times. Put a penny on Saturn.

Move three times. Put a penny on Jupiter.

Move once. Put a penny on the Moon.

Where, now, is the dime?

Answer on page 98.

THINK-A-DIGIT

Choose a digit from 1 through 9. Enter it three times in your calculator. For example, if you picked 8, enter 888.

Divide this number by 3.

Divide the result by the number you thought of.

What number is now on display?

Answer on page 110.

A REMARKABLE NUMBER

Enter 999999 in your calculator, then divide it by seven. The result will be a mysterious number.

Multiply this number by any number obtained by tossing a die.

Arrange the digits of the product in increasing order, starting with the smallest digit, then the next higher one, and so on to the largest digit. This will form a six-digit number.

What is the number?

Answer on page 108.

HEADS OR TAILS?

You need seven pennies for this test. Spin them one at a time on a hard surface. Or, if you prefer, carefully balance all seven pennies on their edge, then bang the table to make them all fall over.

After all seven coins have fallen flat, will there be more heads showing than tails, or vice versa?

Answer on page 103.

DROP THE COIN

Put your two hands together like this.

Ask someone to put a coin between the tips of your third fingers.

If you keep your middle fingers pressed firmly together as shown, you'll find it easy to separate the tips of your thumbs, index fingers, and pinkies.

Can you move the tips of your third fingers apart to let the coin fall?

Answer on page 101.

AT THE APEX

Copy the triangle of circles below.

Put any four digits you like in the four vacant circles of the bottom row. They needn't be all different, and you may include one or more zeros if you like.

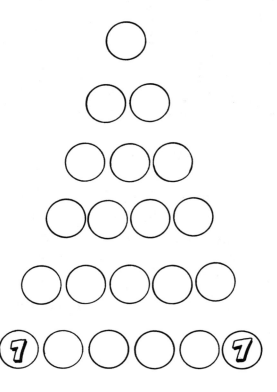

The remaining circles are filled with digits as follows:

Add two adjacent pairs of numbers, divide the sum by 5, and put the remainder in the circle just above the adjacent pair of numbers.

For example, suppose two adjacent numbers in the bottom row are 6 and 8. They add to 14. Dividing 14 by 5 gives a remainder of 4, so you put 4 directly above the 6 and 8. If there is no remainder (such as 6 + 4 = 10, and 10 ÷ 5 = 2) then put a zero above the 6 and 4.

Continue in this way, going up the triangle, until all the circles have digits.

What digit is at the apex of the triangle?

Answer on page 99.

A CALCULATOR TEST

Think of any digit from 1 through 9. Enter it in your calculator.

Multiply it by 11.

Divide the result by the sum of its digits.

What do you get on the display?

Answer on page 99.

A PECULIAR SERIES

Think of a number. It can be of any size. Jot it down.

Add 7 to the number and put the sum down to the right of the chosen number.

Add 7 again to get a third number.

Add 7 once more to get a fourth number. You now have a row of four numbers.

Multiply the two end numbers and write down the product.

Multiply the two middle numbers and write down the product.

Subtract the smaller product from the larger.

What is the result?

Answer on page 107.

ROTATING SPOON

Hold the end of a spoon by the handle, with the bowl of the spoon upside down. Flip the spoon in the air so it makes a complete somersault, and catch it by the end.

It's a good idea to do this over a bed to avoid the

clatter, because you may drop the spoon many times before you succeed in catching it.

When you do catch the handle, will the spoon's bowl be right side up or upside down?

Answer on page 108.

ANOTHER CALCULATOR TEST

Your calculator keyboard has a square of digits from 1 through 9. Select any row, column, or main diagonal.

Arrange the three digits you selected in any order, then jot them down on paper as a three-digit number. For example, if you selected the middle column, you have the digits 852. You can put them in any order you like, such as 528, 285, and so on.

Select another row, column, or main diagonal. Do the same thing with its three digits to make a second three-digit number. Write it down.

Using the calculator, multiply one of the three-digit numbers by the other.

Add all the digits in the product. Call the sum "k".

Refer to the magic circle of symbols on the opposite page. Put your finger on the star, calling it 1, then tap your finger clockwise around the circle, counting, 2, 3, 4, . . . until you reach the number "k".

What symbol did your count stop on?

Answer on page 98.

FOUR QUEENS

Put the four queens on top of the deck, then add eight indifferent cards on top of the queens.

Think of a number from 10 through 19. Deal that many cards from the deck to the table. Add the two digits in the number you selected. Call the sum "k".

Transfer "k" cards from the table back to the top of the deck. Remove the top card of the pile on the table. Without looking at its face, place it aside.

Put the pile back on the deck. Think of another number from 10 through 19, and repeat the procedure just described. Do it two more times, with two other freely chosen numbers.

You now have four face-down cards on the table. Turn them over. What are they?

Answer on page 103.

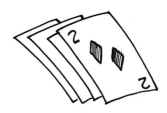

A FOUR-DICE TEST

Place four dice on the table and arrange them so all four top numbers are the same.

Turn two dice upside down and add the top numbers. What's the sum?

Answer on page 102.

A TEST WITH 66

Write down any number from 50 through 100.

Add 66.

Note the last two digits of the sum. Let's call this number "k".

Subtract "k" from the number you first thought of. What's the result?

Just for good measure, do you know why no one played cards on Noah's Ark?

Answers on page 110.

246,913,578

Enter the above "strange" number, the title of this test, into your calculator. Now, you may freely choose to do any of the following:

Multiply the number by 2, 4, 5, 7, 8, 10, 11, 13, 16, 20, 22, 25, 26, 31, 35, 40, 55, 65, 125, 175, or 875!

Or, if you prefer, divide the number by 2, 4, 5, or 8!

After you have done one of the above multiplications or divisions, rearrange the digits of the result in serial order from the smallest digit to the largest. Ignore any zeros among the digits.

The result will be a number of nine digits. What is this number?

Answer on page 112.

FUNNY FRACTIONS

Consider the following compound fraction:

$$\frac{a/b}{c/d}$$

Rearrange the terms to form another compound fraction:

$$\frac{d/c}{b/a}$$

For the terms a, b, c, and d, substitute any digits you like.

Determine the difference between the two compound fractions.

What is it?

Answer on page 103.

TOPSY TURVY FUN

For a change of pace, Professor Picanumba says to try the following stunts on your calculator. After doing the specified multiplications or divisions, turn your calculator around to read its display upside down.

1. Say "Hi!", then divide 6.1872 by 8.

2. What do friends say after you fool them with a magic trick? Divide 31563 by 7.

3. What did Santa Claus say when Rudolph showed him one of these stunts? Multiply .06734 by 6.

4. What's the capital of Idaho? Multiply 8777 by 4.

Answers on page 111.

A TRICK WITH THREE DICE

Toss three dice on the table. Call them A, B, and C.

Write down the total showing on A and B.

Turn B and C upside down and write the total showing.

Turn upside down C and A and write the total.

Add the three sums.

What's the result?

Answer on page 112.

FOUR KINGS

Put the four kings on top of the deck, then cut the deck into four approximately equal piles. The piles should be in a row in front of you, with the pile that was formerly the deck's top on the right end of the row.

Pick up the leftmost pile. Deal three cards into the spot where it stood, then deal a single card on top of each of the other three piles. Replace the rest of the pile on top of the three cards you just dealt, to the spot where the pile was before.

Repeat this same procedure with each of the other three piles.

Turn over the top card of each pile.

What cards are they?

Answer on page 102.

PAIRING CARDS

Deal 28 cards to the table, turn them face up, then shuffle them into the rest of the deck. Shuffle a few

more times to make sure the deck is a random mixture of face-down and face-up cards.

From the top of the deck remove a pair of cards. If one is face up and the other face down, toss the pair aside.

If both cards are face up, put them at the left of the table. If both are face down, put them at the right.

Continue taking cards from the top of the deck in pairs. If the pair is a mixture—one card up, the other down—toss it aside. If both cards are alike, place them left or right as explained.

After you have gone through the entire deck, you will have a pile of face-up cards on the left, and a pile of face-down cards on the right. Count the number of cards in each pile. Subtract the smaller number from the larger.

What's the difference?

Answer on page 107.

WHERE'S THE DIME?

Place a dime or small coin on any of the white squares in the matrix on the opposite page, then make the following moves:

1. Move the dime left or right to the nearest black square.
2. Move the dime up or down to the nearest white square.
3. Move the dime diagonally to the nearest black square.
4. Move the dime either down or to the right to the nearest white square.

On what square is the dime now resting?

Answer on page 113.

WHAT'S THE WORD?

Crease a sheet of paper as shown below and letter the eight cells from A to H.

Fold the sheet into a packet eight leaves deep by folding it any way you like along the creases. After you do this, some cells in the packet will face one way and other cells will face the opposite way. Because you made the folds at random, there seems to be no way to know which cells face which way.

Trim the four edges of the packet with scissors, so that no cell is attached to another cell.

Spread the pieces on the table. Can you arrange the face-up pieces to spell a common English word? If you can, stop. If you can't, turn over all the pieces.

Try again to spell a word with the face-up pieces. You are sure to succeed. What word do you spell?

Answer on page 113.

THREE SURPRISES

Enter 777 in your calculator. Multiply it by your age.

1. Multiply the result by 13. Are you surprised?

2. Now, try this: Enter 1443. Multiply it by your age, then by 7.

3. For a third surprise, enter 3367. Multiply by your age, then by 3.

Answers on page 111.

ANOTHER CALCULATOR SURPRISE

Enter 987654312 in your calculator. Note that the last two numbers, 1 and 2, are interchanged.

Divide by 8. What's the surprise?

As a bonus, Professor Picanumba will tell you how you can throw a ball so it stops in midair, reverses direction, and comes back to you!

Answers on page 98.

A SURPRISING FRACTION

Write down to be added a series of odd numbers in numerical order starting with 1:

1 + 3 + 5 + 7 + 9 + 11 + ...

Continue the series for as many numerical terms as you like, provided the number of terms is even.

Let the first half of the series be the numerator of a fraction, and the second half of the series be the fraction's denominator; for example, if you stopped after six terms the fraction would be:

$$\frac{1 + 3 + 5}{7 + 9 + 11}$$

Add the number of terms above the line, then add the series of terms below the line. Then reduce the fraction you get to its lowest terms.

What fraction do you end up with?

Answer on page 110.

WHERE'S THE ACE?

Find the ace of spades and place it face up on top of the deck.

Think of a number from 10 through 19. Call it "k."

Deal "k" cards to the table. The bottom of the pile you dealt will, of course, be the *face-up* ace of spades. Place this pile on top of the deck.

Add the two digits of "k," then transfer that many cards from the top of the deck to the bottom.

How far down in the deck is the ace of spades?

Answer on page 113.

A LETTER IN WASHINGTON

Multiply together all eight digits in the serial number on a dollar bill. Add all the digits in the product. The sum will have two digits.

Add the two digits. If the result is another 2-digit number, add again. Keep adding until a single digit remains.

Call this digit "k."

Count to the "k"th letter in WASHINGTON.
What's the letter?

Answer on page 104.

FOUR FILE CARDS

Write 39 on one side of a file card, and 51 on the other
side. On a second file card write 26 and 34 on the two
sides. A third card gets 65 and 85. A fourth card gets
52 and 68.

Place the four cards on the table so the numbers
showing on top are 26, 39, 52, and 65.

Slide any card out of the row, then turn over the
three remaining cards. Slide out another card, and turn
over the remaining two cards.

Slide out a third card. Turn over the remaining card.

You now have a choice of leaving the cards as they
are, or turning all of them over.

With your calculator, multiply all the numbers
showing. What's the product?

Answer on page 102.

THE MISSING 8

Enter 12345679 in your calculator. Note that the 8 is missing from the series.

Multiply the series by 3.

Multiply the result by any digit from 1 through 9.

Multiply once more by 3.

What's the surprising result?

Answer on page 105.

AN 8-CARD TEST

Place the six of spades and the ten of hearts back to back and fasten them together with a paper clip.

Do the same thing with the following pairs:

Seven of spades and jack of hearts.

Eight of spades and queen of hearts.

Nine of spades and king of hearts.

Put these four "double-face cards" in a row on the table, hearts side up on all cards. Or, if you prefer, the four may have their spade sides uppermost.

Select any two of the double-face cards and turn them over. Add the values of the cards on top. The jack has a value of 11, the queen 12, and the king 13.

What's the sum?

Answer on page 101.

AN UNEXPECTED NUMBER

This is not a prediction test, but merely a test of your ability to recognize a famous number.

Start with 1234. Switch 1 and 2, and switch 3 and 4, to get 2143. Enter it in your calculator.

Divide by 22, then hit the square root key twice. What do you get?

Answer on page 113.

FIVE COINS

Place on the table in a row, in order from left to right, a penny, dime, nickel, half dollar, and a quarter. (If you don't have a half dollar handy, write "50¢" on a small piece of paper and use it instead of the coin.

Put a marker (small toy, checker, square of cardboard) on any of the five coins. Move it back and forth, from coin to adjacent coin, as many times as indicated by the value of cents in the coin on which you placed it. For example, if you put the marker on the quarter, your first move must be left, but after that you can move it either left or right as you count the moves to 25. If the marker is on the penny, you move it only once, and so on for the other coins.

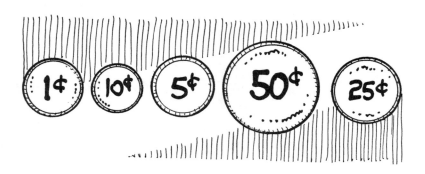

After you have moved the marker the required number of times, Professor Picanumba says the penny will be uncovered. Take away the penny.

Again move the folder a number of times indicated by the coin on which it now rests. The Professor says this will leave the quarter uncovered. Take it away.

Three coins remain. Move the marker once.

On what coin is the marker?

Answer on page 101.

LITTLE PIGGIES

If you divide the number of your toes by ½, then multiply the result by the number of your fingers, what do you get?

Answer on page 105.

THE ROTATING TUBES

Place two paper towel or toilet tissue tubes side by side and balance a yardstick on top.

If you rotate the tubes inward, as shown by the arrows, the yardstick will remain balanced on the tubes. It may shift slightly back and forth, but it stays balanced.

Test it out and see for yourself.

Now, testing your own mental magic, what do you suppose would happen if you tried rotating the two tubes the opposite way; that is, away from each other?

Answer on page 109.

A THREE-DICE STACK

You need three dice for this test. Toss the first die on the table. Toss a second die, pick it up in your fingers, and place it right on top of the first die. The third die then goes on top of the other two, turned so its top face is 1.

If you inspect this stack from all sides, you'll note that five faces cannot be seen. Add these faces as follows:

Check the two touching faces between the top and middle dice. Write down their sum, and put the top die aside.

Check the two hidden faces that are touching between the two dice that remain. Add the numbers, write down the sum, and put the top die aside.

Check the bottom face of the remaining die. Write it down. Add the three numbers you have written.

What's their sum?

Answer on page 111.

ONE, TWO, THREE

Choose a single digit from the numbers 1, 2, and 3.
  Multiply it by the digit 8.
  Subtract 3.
  To the result add the digit you first selected.
  Call the sum "k."
  Count to the "k"th word of these instructions.
  What word is it?

Answer on page 107.

CAPITAL-VILLE

The capital of Kentucky is not pronounced Looey-ville
or Lewis-ville. What's the correct pronunciation?

Answers on page 99.

A 3 BY 4 TEST

Make a copy of this 3 by 4 matrix.
  Put digits 1 through 9 in the cells in any way you
like. Three empty cells will remain. In those cells, put

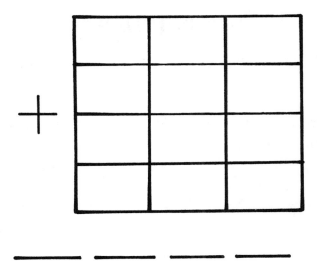

either three ones, three fours, or three sevens.

Treat each row of the matrix as a 3-digit number. Add these four numbers by writing the sum over the four lines below the matrix.

Add the sum's four digits. If the result is more than one digit, add those two numbers. Keep adding until only one digit remains.

What is this digit?

Answer on page 111.

THE CURIOUS Q

Think of a number between 10 and 50, inclusive.

Put your finger on the bottom symbol in the tail of the Q on the facing page. Say "One." Tap the next symbol above it and say "Two." Continue upward, counting at each tap, until you reach the star, then turn right and continue tapping *counterclockwise* around the circle until you say the number you originally thought of. The tapping may take you more than once around the circle. If it does, ignore the tail of the Q as you go around.

After you tap the symbol at the count of your chosen number, pause and reverse direction. You now tap *clockwise* around the circle, ignoring the tail. Say "One" for the symbol you last tapped. Don't make the mistake of starting your count on the symbol next to it. When you reach the number you first selected, note the symbol where the count ends.

What symbol is it?

Answer on page 100.

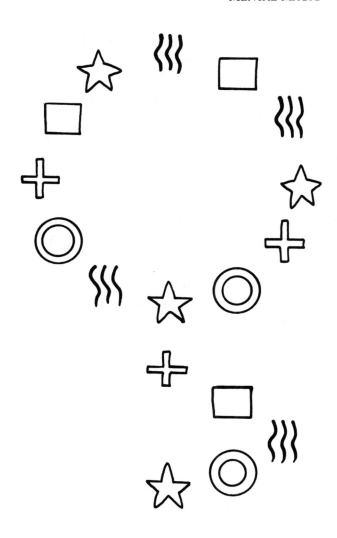

THE FOUR KNIGHTS

Place a penny on each of the four central squares on the checkerboard shown on the opposite page.

The pennies move like the knight piece in chess—that is, two squares up, down, left, or right (not diagonally), then one square at right angles to the previous move.

Select any of the "knights" and move it as many times as indicated by the number on its starting square. Write down the color (black or white), of the cell where it landed. Remove the penny. It is okay for a penny to land on top of another penny.

Repeat this with another penny. After it has moved according to the number on its starting square, again write down the color of the square where it stopped, and take away the penny.

Repeat this procedure with the other two pennies. What are the four colors you have listed?

Answer on page 102.

AROUND THE CIRCLE

Jot down the last two digits of your phone number. Add them, then subtract this sum from the original two-digit number. Call the difference "k."

Put a finger on the cross at the top of the circle of symbols on the opposite page. Say "One." Now tap the symbols clockwise around the circle, counting as you go, until you tap the symbol corresponding to "k."

On what symbol does this count end?

Answer on page 98.

DEAL AND SWITCH

Arrange the spade cards of a deck in order from ace to king, with the ace on top of a packet of thirteen face-down cards.

As you deal these cards to form a face-down pile, mix their order as follows:

Either deal a single card, or take a pair of cards and reverse their positions before you place them on the pile. In other words, at each step you make a choice—either to put a single card on the pile or to put down a pair after you have moved the top card below the other one. The purpose of this procedure is to destroy the ordering of the cards.

After you have gone through all thirteen cards, pick up the pile and repeat the procedure, deciding at random whether to deal one card or a reversed pair.

After this repeat dealing, how are the spades arranged?

Answer on page 100.

INSECT, ANIMAL, BIRD

Think of a foreign country with a name that begins with A. Without taking a long time to think, write down:

1. The name of an insect that begins with the last letter of the country you thought of.

2. A wild animal with a name that starts with the last letter of the insect.

3. A bird that begins with the last letter of the animal.

Answers on page 104.

THE SIX GLASSES

Arrange six drinking glasses in a row. Assume they are numbered 1, 2, 3, 4, 5, 6, from the left. Drop a penny into glass 1. Now, you must move the penny as you spell the professor's name.

A move consists of pouring the penny from one glass to the *nearest* glass on either side.

Spell PROFESSOR by making a move for each letter. When you finish, take away glass 1.

Now spell PICANUMBA. Take away glass 2.

Spell your last name twice. Take away glass 6.

Make one final move.

In what glass is the penny?

Answer on page 109.

END OF A CHAIN

Think of any three-digit number with no two of its digits alike. Write the digits in ascending and descending order. Subtract the smaller number from the larger to get a second number. For example, if you thought of 614 you would subtract 146 from 641.

Arrange the new number's digits in ascending and descending order. Subtract the smaller from the larger to get a third number.

Keep doing this until you reach a number that keeps repeating itself.

What is this number that ends the chain?

Answer on page 101.

A YARDSTICK PREDICTION

Using tape, fasten two quarters, one on top of the other, at one end of a yardstick so they cover the inch from 35 to 36. Rest the yardstick on top of your hands as shown.

Bring your hands together slowly, moving each hand at any speed you like. When your palms touch you will be surprised to find that the yardstick remains balanced on your fingers.

What is the number on the yardstick nearest the spot where your palms touch?

Answer on page 114.

IN PRAISE OF BLUE

Barbara's eyes are a beautiful blue.

On a bluebell, a blue butterfly.

I seldom am blue in December.

Though frequently blue in July.

A blue cheese is tasty on salads.

Blue berries are great in a pie.

But the most wonderful blue of all

Is the blue of a cloudless sky.

Roll a die. The number that comes up indicates a line in the above poem. Now look at the bottom face of the die. This tells you how to count to a word in the selected line.

What word do you reach?

Answer on page 104.

ODD OR EVEN?

Put ten cards face down on the table, spread apart in any pattern you like. Now turn over cards as follows:

Reverse any single card, then reverse any pair of cards, then any three cards, and so on until you reverse all ten cards.

Count the number of face-up cards. Is it odd or even?

Answer on page 107.

A ROW OF NINE

From a deck, remove nine cards with values of ace (one) through nine. Arrange them in a row, face down and in counting order, starting with the ace on the left.

Select a card at either end of the row, and remove it from the row. Turn it face up.

Again, choose either end of the row. Slide the card from the row and turn it over.

Repeat this a third time, again picking a card from either end at random.

Add the values of the three cards randomly selected and removed. Divide the sum by 6. Call the result "n."

Look at the row's "n"th card. What value does it have?

Here's a funny story for you. Ms. Ames was startled to read, in a student's essay, that a neighbor, Mr. Jones, "always walks naked down the street." As quickly as she could, she phoned the student's parents. They confirmed that it was true...then they all laughed! How come?

Answers on page 109.

NINE-CARD SPELL

Remove nine cards from the deck. Shuffle them, then hold them face down in your left hand. Reverse the third card from the top of the packet.

Spell the name of the reversed card as follows. Let's assume it was the queen of hearts.

Spell Q-U-E-E-N by dealing five cards to the table, one card for each letter. Place the remaining cards on top of the five just dealt.

Pick up the packet. Spell O-F by dealing two cards to the table. Again, put the remaining cards on top of those just dealt.

Now spell H-E-A-R-T-S. Put the cards in your hand on top of the tabled pile.

Follow this procedure, using the name of the card you have reversed. Note that the number of letters in the name can vary from 10 (for example, the ace of clubs) to 15 (for example, the eight of diamonds).

After spelling the name of the reversed card, how far down is it from the top of the packet?

Answer on page 106.

LINCOLN UP OR DOWN?

Toss a five dollar bill into the air and let it flutter to the floor. After the bill lands, will the top of the bill show Lincoln's picture?

Answer on page 104.

A ROYAL FINISH

Arrange 26 cards so that face down, from top to
bottom, the packet consists of the ace through king of
hearts, in serial order, followed by the ace through
king of spades, also in serial order.

As you deal the cards face down, stop at any of the
hearts and turn it face up. You may do this with the
ace or king or any heart in between.

Count the number of letters in the name of the card's value. For example, the ace is 3, the two is 3, the three is 5, and so on. Call this number "k," deal "k" more cards, then turn the "k"th card face up. Again count the letters in the name of the card's value, and deal that number of cards, turning face up the card at the end of the count. Continue dealing and counting in this way, reversing a card at the end of each count, until you can't go any further.

What is the last card you turn face up?

Answer on page 109.

TWINKLE, TWINKLE

Believe it or not, you are featured in this familiar poem:

> Twinkle, twinkle, little star,
> How I wonder what you are
> Up above the world so high,
> Like a diamond in the sky.
> Twinkle, twinkle, little star,
> How I wonder what you are.

Select any word in the poem's first two lines. Spell the word by tapping the words ahead in the manner described in this book's first test (page 8). Keep going until your spelling chain can't continue any farther.

On what word does the count end?

Answer on page 112.

THE PROFESSOR PREDICTS

Here are Professor Picanumba's predictions: the answers that he foresaw or said that you would likely give in doing these tests. A marvelous gift to have, isn't it!

An ABCABC Number

The number on display is the three-digit number you first thought of!

Another Calculator Surprise

The surprise is that the digits 1 through 9 are now in serial order starting with 1.

To make the tossed ball come back, toss it straight up in the air.

Another Calculator Test

You stopped your count on the heart.

Around the Circle

The count ends on the spiral.

Around the Solar System

If you moved correctly, the dime is on Pluto.

Around the Square

Your count ended on the letter D.

At the Apex

The triangle's top digit is 4.

Beast, City, Vegetable

Professor Picanumba guesses that the words are lion, Paris, and carrot.

A Calculator Test

The calculator displays 5.5.

Capital-Ville

The correct way to pronounce the capital of Kentucky is Frankfort.

Cards that Shake Dice

The sum of all the dice "throws" is 84.

Catch the Bill

You can't catch the bill before it drops.

Count the Clips

There are six paper clips left in the box.

A Curious Count

The number of undealt cards is 8.

The Curious Q

The last symbol you tapped is the star.

Deal and Switch

The thirteen spades are back in their original order, ace to king, with the ace on top.

A Domino Chain

The spots at the end of the domino chain will be 2 and 5.

Drop the Coin

Impossible, says Professor Picanumba.

An 8-Card Test

The four cards will have a sum of 38.

End of a Chain

The number that ends the chain is 495.

The Exact Word

"The exact word." Sorry about that!

Face-Up Cards

The difference is zero. The number of face-up cards in one pile will exactly equal the number of face-up cards in the other pile!

Five Coins

The marker is on the nickel.

Five in a Row

Professor Picanumba is not always right on this one, but he thinks you selected the four of hearts.

Fold and Trim

The face-up numbers will have the sum of 68.

A Four-Dice Test

The sum of the top faces of the four dice is 14.

Four File Cards

The product of the numbers on the file cards is 5,860,920.

Four Kings

The four cards on top of each pile are the four kings.

The Four Knights

The four colors are each white.

Four Queens

The four cards are the four queens!

Funny Fractions

The difference is zero.

A Geometry Test

Professor Picanumba isn't sure, but he suspects you either put a circle inside a triangle, or a triangle inside a circle.

The GRY Test

The word you thought of was either "hungry" or "angry."
  You were born within four days of Wednesday, and the cowboy's horse was named Friday.

Heads or Tails?

There will be more heads than tails.

In Praise of Blue

The word is "blue."

In Praise of Red

The word is "red."

Insect, Animal, Bird

Professor Picanumba guesses that you wrote ant, tiger, and robin.

A Letter in Washington

The letter in Washington is O. Professor Picanumba isn't positive he got this right, but he is almost certain he did.

Lincoln Up or Down?

The answer is yes. Professor Picanumba apologizes for this "swindle" because no matter which way the bill falls, he can't lose. On the back of the five dollar bill there is another picture of Lincoln. It shows him seated in front of the Lincoln Memorial in Washington, D.C.

Little Piggies

The answer to the riddle is not 50, but 200. Ten divided by ½ is 20.

The Magic of 8

The final digit is 8.

The Missing 8

The digit you selected is repeated in the display nine times. Professor Picanumba adds: Try dividing any digit except 0 by 9.

Monkey Business

You'd have six bananas left. (It's important to read tests carefully.)

A Mysterious Matrix

The sum of the six circled numbers is 111.

Nation, Animals, Fruit

The five words are Denmark, elephant, gray, kangaroo, and orange.

As for your shoes, you got 'em on your feet!

Nine-Card Spell

The reversed card is fifth from the top.

Number, Flower, Color

Professor Picanumba isn't positive, but his best guesses are 37, rose, and blue.

Number Names

The number that ends the chain is 4.

Odd or Even?

The number of face-up cards is odd.

One, Two, Three

The word is "the."

Pairing Cards

The difference is four. There will be four more cards in the face-down pile than there are cards in the face-up pile.

A Peculiar Series

The result is 98.

The Red and the Black

The difference between the black and red cards is 4.

The product of all ten digits is zero.

A Remarkable Number

The six-digit number is 124578.

Reverse, Subtract, Add

The word is "star."

The Rotated Die

The sum is odd.

A Rotating Matrix

The count ended on a cross.

Rotating Spoon

Professor Picanumba says that no matter how hard you try, when you catch the spoon its bowl will be right side up. He says he doesn't know why this is always the case.

The Rotating Tubes

The yardstick travels to one side until it falls off the tubes.

A Row of Nine

The row's "n"th card is four.

Mr. Jones was walking his dog Naked, a perfectly capital, fine thing to do. (Remember to capitalize proper nouns.)

A Royal Finish

The card at the end of your counting chain is the king of spades.

The Six Glasses

The penny is in the middle glass of the three remaining glasses.

A Surprising Fraction

The final fraction is ⅓.

A Surprising Sum

The total of the four random numbers is 22,222.

A Test with 66

The result is 34.

There was no card playing on the Ark because Noah sat on the deck.

A Test with Two Dice

The sum of the four products is 49.

A Test with Your Age

The number on display is 238.

Think-a-Digit

The number on display is 37.

Think-a-Letter

The letter will be the letter you first thought of.

A 3 by 4 Test

The final digit is 3.

A Three-Dice Stack

The sum of the five hidden faces is 20.

Three Heaps

The number of clips in the center heap is 10.

Three Surprises

In each case the result is your age repeated three times.

Topsy Turvy Fun

The upside-down words are HELLO, GOSH, HO-HO-HO, and BOISE.

A Trick With Three Dice

The result is 21.

Try This on a Dollar Bill

The final digit is 2.

Turn Two and Cut

There are five face-up cards in the row.

Twinkle, Twinkle

The count ends on "you."

A Two-Dice Test

The final sum is 21.

246,913,578

The number is 123456789.

An Unexpected Number

You get pi (the circumference of a circle with a diameter of 1) correct to eleven decimal places except for the ninth decimal, which should be 3 instead of 2.

What's on the Paper?

You are on the paper.

To see through walls, look through a window.

What's the Word?

The word you spell is CAGE.

Where's the Ace?

The ace of spades will be the ninth card from the top.

Where's the Dime?

The dime is on square K.

Whisk the Dime

The dime refuses to be brushed off your palm.

The riddle's answer is that the barber would make ten times as much money.

Wonderland Spell

The word is "sister."

A Yardstick Prediction

Your palms come together at the 21 mark.

BRAIN TEASERS

EAGLE EYES

In each grid, there is one letter that is repeated twice. Find the repeated letter and write it in the numbered space that matches the grid number. Then read the letters from 1 to 8 to answer this riddle: What drink does a tree like?

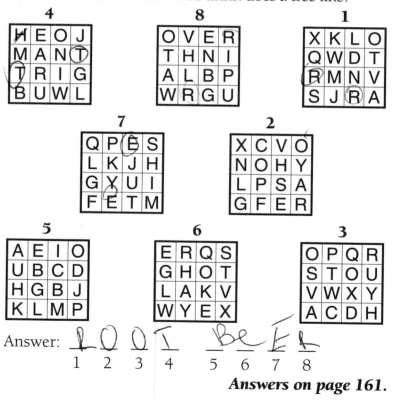

4

H	E	O	J
M	A	N	T
T	R	I	G
B	U	W	L

8

O	V	E	R
T	H	N	I
A	L	B	P
W	R	G	U

1

X	K	L	O
Q	W	D	T
R	M	N	V
S	J	R	A

7

Q	P	E	S
L	K	J	H
G	X	U	I
F	E	T	M

2

X	C	V	O
N	O	H	Y
L	P	S	A
G	F	E	R

5

A	E	I	O
U	B	C	D
H	G	B	J
K	L	M	P

6

E	R	Q	S
G	H	O	T
L	A	K	V
W	Y	E	X

3

O	P	Q	R
S	T	O	U
V	W	X	Y
A	C	D	H

Answer: R O O T B E E R

1   2   3   4   5   6   7   8

Answers on page 161.

FOUND LETTERS

What noisy pig is a great movie director? For the answer to this riddle, find the one letter in the word in the right-hand column that's *not* in the word in the left-hand column. Write the extra letter on the blank space. Then read *down* the column.

LATTER	S	STARTLE
PARENT		PATTERN
SPACE	E	ESCAPE
TUREEN	V	VENTURE
RAPPER	E	PREPARE
AGREED	N	ANGERED
CLIENT	S	STENCIL
SUET	Q	QUEST
SANDY	U	SUNDAY
VERSE	E	SEVERE
HORNET	A	ANOTHER
WIVES	L	SWIVEL
EARLY	B	BARLEY
THEIR	E	EITHER
IMPOSE	R	PROMISE
LEANER	G	ENLARGE

Answers on page 163.

SO SYMBOL

Instead of typing out each of the listed words, we substituted symbols for a few of the letters. Can you figure out each word? Hint: Spell out the symbols, and you'll have no problem!

1. C A 9 _~~anine~~_
2. C @ A L O G _~~catalog~~_
3. ✔ E R S _~~checkers~~_
4. — I N G _~~dashing~~_
5. = I T Y _____
6. H & S O M E _____
7. P E R ¢ A G E _____
8. S P ➡ _____
9. ★ T L E D _____
10. S U R + _____
11. T E L E P H 1 _____
12. 10 A N T S _____
13. W 8 L I F T E R _____

Answers on page 164.

MINI FILL-INS

Complete each grid by putting the words into the spaces where they belong.

Sports

ARCHERY   ROWING

GOLF   RUGBY

HOCKEY   SOCCER

POLO

Drinks

EGGNOG   SELTZER

LEMONADE   TEA

MILK   WATER

MOCHA

NECTAR

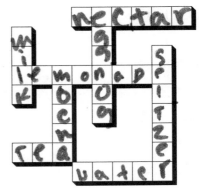

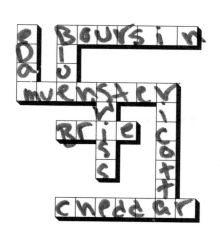

Cheeses

BLUE

BOURSIN

BRIE

CHEDDAR

EDAM

MUENSTER

RICOTTA

SWISS

Dances

BOLERO   LIMBO

CONGA   POLKA

HORA   TAP

HULA

Answers on page 165.

ONE FROM COLUMN A

Take one word from Column A plus one word from Column B plus one word from Column C to make a new word. Write the new word in the space provided. Cross off each word as you use it, for it will only be used once. The first one is done for you.

COLUMN A	COLUMN B	COLUMN C	NEW WORD
1. CAP	IT	TIC	CAPACITY
2. CAR	MAN	SHIP	*carmel*
3. CHAR	ON	OW	_____
4. DRAG	BID	MINT	_____
5. FOR	MALL	METER	_____
6. GIG	A	FLY	_____
7. MARSH	PER	EL	_____
8. PEN	AN	DEN	_____
9. PEP	O	CITY	_____
10. THERM	AM	ABLE	_____

Answers on page 166.

BIRD WATCHING

Eighteen birds are hidden in these nonsense sentences. To find them, search between two or more words. Underline each bird when you find it. **OWL** is nesting in the first sentence.

1. H<u>OW L</u>OVELY YOU LOOK!
2. PLEASE SEND OVER THAT PICTURE.
3. THE SHIP'S SPAR ROTATED EASILY.
4. THAT FELLOW RENTED A CAR.
5. THEY FOUND THE LOST RICHES.
6. DRIVE FAST OR KEEP TO THE RIGHT.
7. SAY HELLO ONCE MORE.
8. GIVE ME A DOLLAR KELLY.
9. HERE'S THE CHAPEL I CAN ATTEND.
10. A FABRIC LIKE LYCRA NEEDS VERY LITTLE CARE.
11. CAN A RYE BREAD BE MADE AT HOME?
12. PUT YOUR BUSINESS CARD IN ALBERT'S HAND.
13. SHE'S WANDERING AWAY.
14. THEY CRAVE NEW FOODS.
15. DRINK THE TEA GLENDA BROUGHT.
16. HE GREW ONE HALF INCH.
17. THE CHEF AL CONTACTED IS COOKING DINNER.
18. UNTHAW KIM'S SUPPER.

Answers on page 167.

CHANGEOVER #1

Anagrams are words in which the letters of one word are shuffled around to make a new word, like ANIMAL and MANILA. Find the anagrams to all the listed words, then read *down* the first letter of each new word to find two things that are always changing. Write the answers on the lines below each list. Note: Each new word will start with a *different* letter than the original word.

1. LEAF _Feal_

2. BALE _able_

3. OURS _sour_

4. THIN _hint_

5. AIDE _idea_

6. CONE _once_

7. TONE _not_

8. LOSE _sole_

Answer: _____

_____

1. KISS _____

2. AGREE _____

3. CHASE _____

4. HOST _____

5. CANOE _____

6. THING _____

7. VOTES _____

Answer: _____

_____

Answers on page 168.

TOP GUY

The President of the United States is the most powerful person in the world. To find one of these top guys, put each state's name into the grid in alphabetical order. Then read *down* the starred column. Note: When putting two-word states into the grid, ignore the spacing.

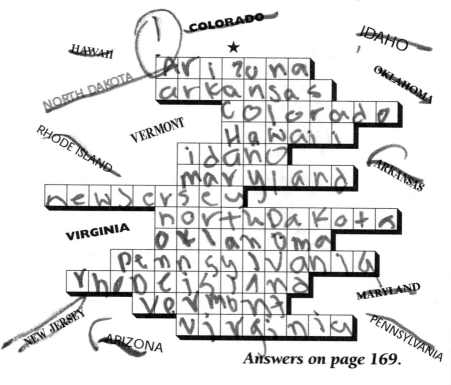

Answers on page 169.

NAME THAT WORD

Each three-letter name (or nickname) in the box will fit into one of the spaces below to form a word described in the parentheses ( ). The first one has been done for you.

1. B A N N E R (streamer)
2. _Bea_ G L E (a dog like Snoopy)
3. _Ben_ E A T H (below)
4. _Cal_ C U L A T O R (math device)
5. C _art_ O O N (animated movie)
6. C R E _Amy_ (smooth and soft)
7. _Dan_ G E R O U S (risky)
8. _Del_ I G H T F U L (wonderful)
9. D E S T _roy_ (ruin)
10. E N _joy_ M E N T (pleasure)
11. _Eva_ P O R A T E (disappear)
12. F O R _mal_ (dressy event)
13. G _ian_ T (tall monster)
14. I D O _liz_ E (adore)
15. P R E _sid_ E N T (the head of the U.S.A.)
16. S _tom_ A C H (belly)

~~AMY~~	~~ANN~~
~~ART~~	~~BEA~~
~~BEN~~	~~CAL~~
~~DAN~~	~~DEL~~
EVA	~~IAN~~
JOY	~~LIZ~~
MAL	~~ROY~~
~~SID~~	~~TOM~~

Answers on page 170.

ALL WET

What is Frankenstein's favorite waterway? To find the answer to this riddle, put a letter into each blank to name a watery place on each line. Then read down the starred column.

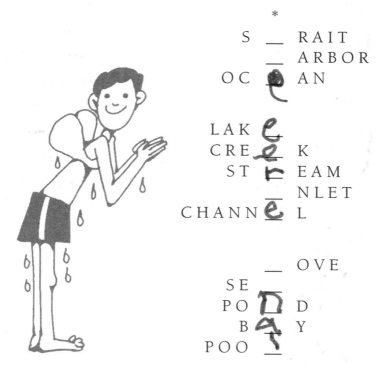

```
              *
     S  __  R A I T
        __  A R B O R
    O C  e  A N

    L A K  e
    C R E  e  K
      S T  r  E A M
        __  N L E T
    C H A N N  e  L

        __  O V E
      S E
      P O  n  D
        B  a  Y
    P O O  l
```

Answers on page 161.

GRIDLOCK

Place one of the foreign cities below onto the blanks in the middle of each "letter box" to spell out 6 five-letter words reading *downwards*.

LONDON	MADRID	MONACO
MUSCAT	ODESSA	OTTAWA

C	S	R	C	L	S
O	T	A	R	U	H
–	–	–	–	–	–
M	R	G	Z	K	R
A	K	E	Y	Y	E

L	R	S	L	W	B
O	A	L	A	A	R
–	–	–	–	–	–
S	A	E	S	T	V
E	R	T	O	E	E

S	P	B	G	L	C
H	U	A	U	O	H
–	–	–	–	–	–
V	T	C	V	E	M
E	Y	H	A	R	P

T	S	B	H	Q	F
U	T	A	U	U	U
–	–	–	–	–	–
M	R	G	R	T	G
Y	K	E	Y	E	E

L	E	F	B	B	M
E	Q	U	A	R	O
–	–	–	–	–	–
O	A	S	O	K	T
N	L	Y	N	E	O

S	W	P	B	G	S
I	H	A	U	R	I
–	–	–	–	–	–
L	L	I	D	W	C
Y	E	C	Y	L	E

Answers on page 164.

CLOSE RELATIVES

Change one letter in each word to find three words that belong together in each group. Write the new words on the lines. The first one is done for you.

1. Vehicles

JAR _____CAR_____

VAL _____

LAB _____

2. Things to Read

HOVEL _____

STORK _____

HAIRY BALE _____

3. Desserts

PADDING _____

TIE _____

ROOKIES _____

4. Females

GILL _____

LAZY _____

ROMAN _____

5. Languages

HERMAN _____

DRENCH _____

CREEK _____

6. Furniture

DISK _____

SODA _____

SABLE _____

7. U.S. Presidents

CARTEL _____

GRUNT _____

BASH _____

8. Males

BAY _____

LID _____

MELLOW _____

9. Reporters' Questions

THERE? _____

WHET? _____

WAY? _____

10. Fowl

THICKEN _____

HEM _____

BOOSTER _____

11. Colors

BED _____

WHINE _____

BLUR _____

12. Animal Sounds

PARK _____

PINK _____

BOO _____

13. Board Games

CHEST _____

SCRIBBLE _____

CLUB _____

14. States

NOW PORK _____

IONA _____

OLIO _____

Answers on page 162.

FILLING STATION

There's a riddle and answer hidden here. To find
them, figure out the answer to each clue given in the
parentheses ( ) below. The numbers on each line tell
you the number of letters in the answer. Write the
word on the space provided after the clue and also
place the letters in the numbered spaces of the
"filling station." Be sure to match up the numbers
correctly.

Clues:

1, 2, 3 (placed in a secret spot) = _____

4, 5, 6 (opposite of him) = _____

7, 8, 9 (everything) = _____

10, 11, 12, 13 (finished) = _____

14, 15, 16, 17 (existence) = _____

18, 19, 20, 21, 22 (what dentists work on) = _____

_____

23, 24, 25 (moist) = _____

W _ Y D _ _ T _ _ _ A M F _ _ _
  1   2 3   4 5 6   7 8 9

_ _ _ _ A C _ _ _ F ? H _ D I D N ' _
10 11 12 13   14 15 16   17   18

S _ _ _ _ E E _ _ _ U R N .
19 20 21 22   23 24 25

Answers on page 166.

FABRIC-ATION

Use the grid below and cross out every word that names a fabric. On most of the lines there will be some extra letters left after you cross out these words. When you're finished, read the remaining letters, from left to right and top to bottom, to finish this joke: Did you hear about the boy who fell into an upholstery machine? Write the words on the blanks below the grid.

F	E	L	T	H	F	L	A	N	N	E	L
E	C	O	R	D	U	R	O	Y	I	S	F
W	O	O	L	C	A	S	H	M	E	R	E
V	E	L	V	E	T	U	S	U	E	D	E
R	A	Y	O	N	C	O	T	T	O	N	L
L	N	Y	L	O	N	Y	R	S	I	L	K
C	H	I	N	T	Z	E	D	E	N	I	M
O	R	G	A	N	D	Y	O	R	L	O	N
L	I	N	E	N	T	A	F	F	E	T	A
C	O	C	H	E	N	I	L	L	E	V	E
C	H	E	E	S	E	C	L	O	T	H	R
E	S	E	E	R	S	U	C	K	E	R	D

Answer: __ __   __ __   __ __ __ __

__ __ __ __ __ __ __ __

Answers on page 166.

POP STARS

Each nonsense phrase rhymes with the first and last names of a well-known person or group in the entertainment industry. Figure out each name (or musical group) and write it in the space provided. There's a hint in the parentheses ( ) on each line.

1. GRAD MITT _B P_ (husband of Jennifer Aniston)

2. JITNEY SHEARS _Britney S_ (pop superstar)

3. PIXIE STICKS _D C_ (female singing trio)

4. CREW TARRYBORE _D B_ (she was a movie star at 8)

5. HIM MARRY _J C_ (he played The Grinch)

6. MERRY MUSSEL _____ (star of "Felicity")

7. SICK BAGGER _____ (a Rolling Stone)

8. PICKY CARTON _____ (a Latino superstar)

9. NICE PEARLS _____ (female singing group)

10. HILL PITH _W Sm_ (actor who starred in "Men In Black")

Answers on page 168.

COSMETIC SURGERY

Take each body part, add or subtract the letters as indicated and rearrange them to make a word that fits the clue. Unlike real cosmetic surgery, this one won't cost you an arm and a leg!

1. STOMACH - HOM = Meowing animals = _____

2. CHEST + ARE = Dishonest people = *Cheaters*

3. FEET + AD = Win a victory over someone = *Defeat*

4. HEART + AEKQU = strong shaking of the ground = *earthquake*

5. ADENOIDS - AD = Phonograph inventor, Thomas = _____

6. FACE + ORST = Predict, like the weather = *forecast*

7. ARM + GENTS = Clothes = _____

8. LOBE + BSG = Turkey sounds = *gobble*

9. EAR + SLI = Middle Eastern country = _____

10. LEG + NEDS = Myths = *legends*

Answers on page 168.

END/START

You can add the same word to each letter group to make the end of one word and the start of another word. Just take each 3-letter word from the box below and place it in the blank spaces on each line to finish one word and start another word. Cross off each word as you use it. Warning: The word you put into the blank space *must* work for both sets of letters.

ADO	AGE	ANT	BAT	CAB	FIT	GAL
HER	ICE	KIN	LOG	MAN	NET	OFF
OUT	PAD	PER	SIT	SUM	TIC	

1. A C R O _ _ _ T E R Y

2. B A B Y _ _ _ U A T E

3. B A Y O _ _ _ W O R K

4. B E N E _ _ _ N E S S

5. B U T C _ _ _ O I N E

6. C A T A _ _ _ I C A L

7. C O O K _ _ _ S I D E

8. D I S T _ _ _ O N Y M

9. F R A N _ _ _ K L E D

10. G A R B _ _ _ N D A S

11. I L L E _ _ _ L E R Y

12. J U S T _ _ _ B E R G

13. K N E E _ _ _ D L E D

14. O P O S _ _ _ M A R Y

15. P O S T _ _ _ H O L E

16. P U M P _ _ _ G D O M

17. S H O W _ _ _ I C E R

18. S K I P _ _ _ F U M E

19. T A X I _ _ _ I N E T

20. T O R N _ _ _ P T E D

Answers on page 169.

BLANKETY BLANK

Fill in the blank space on each line to make a common nine-letter word. Then read down the column to find the answer to this riddle: What famous sheriff started a chain of hotels?

BIRD H OUSE
CUBB Y HOLE
QUOT A TION
SHOR T CAKE
RACE T RACK

LITT L RBUG
NECT E RINE
PAPE R BACK
HEAD _ HONE

Answers on page 161.

JUST THE SAME

Fill in the blank lines with a word that has almost the same meaning as the word in the left column. The new word will answer the clue inside the parentheses.

1. LABYRINTH   A _m a z e_ M E N T
(astonishment)

2. UNACCOMPANIED   B _l o n e l_ Y
(sandwich meat)

3. HELP   B R _a i d_ (pigtail)

4. POUR   B _r a i n_ S T O R M (great idea)

5. FINISH   C A L _e n d_ A R (date book)

6. HURT   C _h a r m_ I N G (delightful)

7. MOUND   C _h i l l_ Y (cold)

8. FAD   C O U _r a g e_ (bravery)

9. WRINKLE   D E _c r e a s e_ (get smaller)

10. BLANKET   D I S _c o v e r_ (find)

11. UNCOOKED   D _r a w_ E R (part of a bureau)

12. PUDGY   _ _ _ _ I G U E (tiredness)

13. ACQUIRE   F O R _g e t_ (fail to remember)

14. POSSESS   F R _o w n_ E D (made a mad face)

15. CUSHION   _mat_ T R E S S
(what you sleep on)

16. HAZE   _ _ _ _ A K E (error)

17. ANGRY   N O _mad_ (wanderer)

18. WEALTHY   O S T _i c h_ (large bird)

19. FRIEND   _pal_ A C E (royal house)

20. ATTEMPT   P A N _t r y_ (place to store food)

21. SIZZLING   P _h o t_ O G R A P H (picture)

22. ABOVE   P R _ _ _ _ B (old saying)

23. SIMPLE   Q U _ _ _ _ (nauseated)

24. FEWER   R E S T _l e s s_ (unable to sit still)

25. EVERYTHING   S C _a l l_ O P S (seafood)

26. AUTOMOBILE   S _c a r_ C E (rare)

27. TINY   S _ _ _ T (sugary)

28. VICTORY   S _ _ _ D L E (cheat)

29. TEAR   T _ _ _ O D (camera stand)

30. SHOUT   _y e l l_ O W (color of bananas)

Answers on page 168.

PARTNERS

There's a nonsense phrase on each line. However, if you change just one letter in each word, you can find real partners on each line. For example, MALT & POPPER would be changed to SALT & PEPPER.

1. MOP & FAD _Mom 3 dad_

2. MORK & JEANS _Pork Beans_

3. COFFER & DREAM _Coffee Cream_

4. NORSE & MARRIAGE _horse carriage_

5. CUR & DRIVEL _car & driver_

6. SABLE & CHAINS _____

7. BAY & GILL _Boy girl_

8. SNOB & FLEET _Snow Sleet_

9. WAIL & SHOVER _Nail & novel_

10. SHIRK & LIE _Shirt & tie_

11. RED & FEEL _____

12. SHOPS & HOCKS _____

13. SILK & ROOKIES _____

14. BATON & EGOS _Bacon Eggs_

15. BRINE & GLOOM _____

Answers on page 169.

DAFFYNITIONS

Don't look for any of these definitions in the dictionary, because they won't be there. Instead, match up each word on the left with one of the daffynitions on the right. You'll be looking for the smaller words that make up each listed word. Example: Adverse = a rhyme in a commercial (ad + verse). Write the letter of the daffynition in the blank space on each line.

1. Adverse   **E**   A. What to do with curly hair
2. Allied   **I**   B. Sound of a guy cracking up
3. Buckskin   __   C. Mom's bed
4. Carnation   __   D. Ruin the metal
5. Chopsticks   __   E. Rhyme in a commercial
6. Fatally   __   F. Beep an insect
7. Grimace   __   G. Overweight pal
8. Manslaughter   __   H. Nothing section
9. Martin   __   I. Former Vice-President Gore fibbed
10. Mascot   __   J. Cannot
11. Notable   __   K. Auto land
12. Ozone   __   L. Deer's relative
13. Padlock   __   M. Cuts up insects
14. Pageant   __   N. Serious pilot
15. Permit   __   O. Fastener on a writing tablet

Answers on page 170.

MAN, OH, MAN!

Man seems to be everywhere, at least in this collection of words. Can you figure out the words from the clues in parentheses?

1. __ __ __ M A N __ __ __   (officer in the navy)

2. __ __ __ __ M A N   (person who puts out blazes)

3. __ __ __ M A N __   (country in Europe)

4. __ __ __ M A N __ __   (capital of Nepal)

5. M A N _ager_   (person in charge of a store)

6. M A N _go_   (juicy tropical fruit)

7. M A N _hatta__ __   (New York City)

8. M A N __ __ __ __ __   (a search for a criminal)

9. M A N __ __ __ __   (lunatic)

10. M A N _acure_   (nail treatment)

11. M A N __ __ __ __   (capital of the Philippines)

12. M A N _dtora_   (large house)

13. M A N _ual_   (instruction book)

14. __ __ __ M A N   (President Harry)

15. _wo_ M A N   (lady)

Answers on page 166.

MONKEY IN THE MIDDLE

Place one of the words in the box on each line to make the end of a phrase (or compound word) with the word on the left and the start of a phrase (or compound word) with the word on the right. Example: If you placed the word time in this space: FATHER _____ LINE, you would make Father Time and Time Line.

CROSS	BALL	WATER	BILL	YARD
PAN	NECK	CHECK	HORSE	TOOTH
BAG	STICK	LIGHT	BUTTON	

1. TEA _____BAG_____ PIPE

2. TENNIS _____BALL_____ GAME

3. DOLLAR _____Bill_____ BOARD

4. PUSH _____Button_____ HOLE

5. BLANK _____Check_____ LIST

6. CRISS _____Cross_____ WORD

7. ROCKING _____Horse_____ RADISH

8. FLASH _____Light_____ HOUSE

9. TURTLE _Neck_ LACE

10. FRYING _Pan_ CAKE

11. LIP _Stick_ FIGURE

12. SWEET _Tooth_ PICK

13. MINERAL _Water_ MELON

14. GRAVE _Yard_ SALE

Answers on page 161.

EXPRESS YOURSELF

Some common terms are written here according to
what they represent. For example, tim would
represent TINY TIM. Can you figure out each one?
Note: There's a list of hints on page 145.

1. WEAR
  LONG

2. K
  E
  E
  R
  C
  A

3. T
  O
  W
  N

4. THEMALCOLMMIDDLE

5. women ~~little women~~

6. SHOT *Big shot*

7. one one one one one one
  the other the other the other
  the other the other the other

8. E K O R T·S

9. GEGS

10. I S L A N D

11. R E A D I N G

12. pound   pound   pound   pound   pound
            weight

13. S T R E E T   T E E R T S

14. heart ed *Broken hearted*

15. tomorrowtheday

EXPRESS YOURSELF HINTS

Answers on page 163

1. Thermal clothing
2. In trouble
3. City area
4. TV show that first aired in 2000
5. Book by Louisa May Alcott
6. Important person
7. Equivalent
8. One way to swim
9. Breakfast dish
10. Area of New York State
11. Understand
12. Dieter's concern
13. Traffic sign
14. Unhappy in love
15. Time

words unexpressed

OPPOSITE DISTRACTION

Fill in the blank lines with a word that means the *opposite* of the word inside the brackets [ ]. The new word you make will answer the clue inside the parentheses ( ).

1. [WIN]   C _LOSE_ T (storage area)

2. [SHUT]   C _OPEN_ H A G E N (city in Denmark)

3. [DOWN]   P _UP_ P E T (marionette)

4. [FAT]   _THIN_ K E R S (people who use their brains)

5. [IN]   M _OUT_ H (part of the face)

6. [OVER]   B L _UNDER_ (mistake)

7. [YOUNG]   C _OLD_ E R (chillier)

8. [ON]   C _OFF_ I N (funeral box)

9. [NICE]   _MEAN_ D E R (wander around)

10. [DARK]   _LIGHT_ N I N G (it goes with thunder)

11. [RURAL]   T _URBAN_ (headdress worn by Muslims)

12. [UNCERTAIN] P L E A _S U R E_ (enjoyment)

13. [EARLY] P _L a t e_ S (dishes)

14. [SUBTRACT] L _a d d_ E R (climbing device)

15. [HARD] G R _e a s e_ (oily)

16. [MANY] C U R _f e w_ (formal time limit)

17. [HIGH] B E _l o w_ (under)

18. [SHORT] P R O _L o n_ g (extend)

19. [COME] T A N _g o_ (ballroom dance)

20. [FANCY] E X _p l a i n_ (make something clear)

21. [BREAK] P R E _f i x_ (letters that come before a word)

22. [FUTURE] _P a s t_ U R E (meadow for cows to graze)

23. [GIVE] O V E R _t a k e_ (pass the car ahead of you)

24. [STAND] D E P O S _i t_ (put money in the bank)

25. [WHISPER] W A S _h o u t_ (complete disaster)

Answers on page 165.

CHANGEOVER #2

Anagrams are words in which the letters of one word are shuffled around to make a new word, like DANGER and GARDEN. Find the anagrams to all the listed words, then read *down* the first letter of each new word to find two things that you are often changing. Write the answers on the lines below each list. Note: Each new word will start with a *different* letter than the original word.

1. GABLE _____ *Bauk*

2. CADET _____ *acted*

3. WORTH _____ *throw*

4. SHEET _____ *these*

5. HEART _____ *earth*

6. DIRE _____ *ride*

7. CHIT _____ *hittith*

8. LEASE _____ *tosh*

9. WORDS _____ *sword*

Answer: _____ *Batteries*

1. DOOR _____ *odor*

2. LUMP _____ *plum*

3. CHIN _____ *inch*

4. EARN _____ *near*

5. DICE _____ *iced*

6. ROVE _____ *over*

7. STUN _____ *nuts*

8. KISS _____ *skies*

Answer: _____

Answers on page 170.

ISLE AISLE

Put one letter into each blank space on a line to form an everyday 5-letter word. Then read down the column to find the name of an island off the coast of Massachusetts.

BU _N_ CH
SC _A_ RF
HI _N_ GE
BA _T_ HE
SK _U_ NK
LU _C_ KY
JO _K_ ER
SW _E_ AT
ME _T_ ER

Answers on page 161.

PEO/PLE/ASERS

From the boxed list below, select three-letter pieces that will do double duty: *finish* the name of a well-known person and start an ordinary word. Put each three-letter word section in the blank spaces on each line. If it *finishes* a last name and *begins* an ordinary word, you've got it right! Cross off each three-letter piece as you use it. One was done for you.

ART	ATT	DUP	EAR	ERA
HER	NES	ORD	SER	TER
TON	UMP	UNT	VIS	~~WIN~~

1. A L E C   B A L D / W I N / T E R

2. A N D R E   B R A U G / _ _ _ / O I N E

3. B E N J A M I N   B R / _ _ _ / A C K

4. B I L L   C L I N / _ _ _ / I G H T

5. B I L L Y   C R U / _ _ _ / L I C A T E

6. B R E N D A N   F R A / _ _ _ / V A N T

7. C A L I S T A   F L O C K H / _ _ _ / I S T

8. CHRISTINA AGUIL/ _ _ _/SER

9. CLAIRE DA/ _ _ _/TLED

10. DEREK JE/ _ _ _/MINAL

11. DONALD TR/ _ _ _/IRE

12. GEENA DA/ _ _ _/ITOR

13. HARRISON F/ _ _ _/INARY

14. HEATHER LOCKL/ _ _ _/LY

15. HELEN H/ _ _ _/IL

Answers on page 166.

CROSS-OFFS

Cross off each word described in the clues. Then read
the leftover letters from *right to left* and *bottom to top* to
find the answer to this riddle: What do farmers learn
in school? Wait! One last thing: Before the answer will
make any sense to you, you have to change *one letter* in
each leftover word!

Cross off:

A. 4 baby animals   **E.** 4 directions

B. 4 anagrams of CATER   **F.** 2 office jobs

C. 4 California cities   **G.** 3 holidays

D. 3 snack foods

WRING   WEST   TRACE   SOUTH   BUNNY

FROG   CANDY   CARET   SACRAMENTO

EAST   CRATE   CLERK   CHRISTMAS

CHIPS   KITTEN   OAKLAND   PIPE

KWANZA   BELL   JOEY   PASADENA   GO

HANUKKAH   RECEPTIONIST   REACT

PUPPY   PRETZELS   NORTH   NOW   FRESNO

Answers on page 170.

ANNA'S GRAM

Use the same 4 letters in each blank space to form words that will make somewhat sensible sentences. Example: Don't M O P E if your P O E M doesn't win first prize.

1. The **boss** hates when anyone in the office is unhappy and **sobs**.
2. They really don't **care** who wins the bicycle **race**.
3. The three **pals** are good friends and would never **slap** or punch each other.
4. One little **part** of the mouse **trap** needs to be fixed.
5. She is sure to **grin** broadly when she gets her new pearl **ring**.
6. **none** of the people like the bright **neon** light.
7. Make sure the boat doesn't **leak** before you take it on the **lake**.
8. They came in **late** and didn't hear the start of the fairy **tale**.
9. If you don't **calm** down you won't get any **clam** chowder.

Answers on page 169.

NUMBER FUN

Each "equation" below stands for a common term involving numbers. Can you figure out each one? There is a topic heading with each group of phrases, and the first one is done for you.

Time

60 S. in a M. = 60 seconds in a minute

60 M. in an H.

24 H. in a D.

7 D. in a W.

31 D. in a M. except for F., A., J., S., and N.

365 D. in a Y.

10 Y. in a D.

4 S. in a Y.

Literature

S. W. and the 7 D.

G. and the 3 B.

T. 3 L. P.

Money

100 P. in a D.

20 N. in a D.

10 D. in a D.

4 Q. in a D.

2 H.D. in a D.

History and Government

13 O. C.

9 J. on the S. C.

2 S. from each S.

Sports

9 I. in a B. G.

18 H. on a G. C.

Weights and Measures
12 I. in a F.
16 O. in a P.

Transportation
4 W. on a C.
2 W. on a B.

Science
9 P. in the S. S.

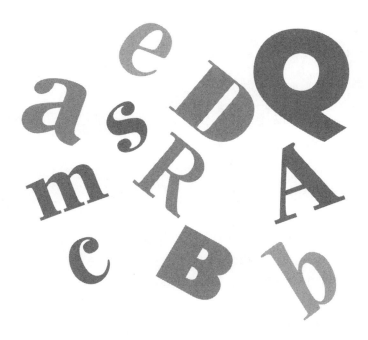

Answers on page 162.

LOW TECH

Answer each clue and write the answers on the numbered spaces. Then move the numbered letters to the *same*-numbered spaces in the answer section on the next page. Work back and forth between the clues and the answer section to find a riddle and its answer.

Clues

A. Someone who seats you in a theater U S h e r
20 49 2 56 29

B. Select C h o o s e
22 42 36 58 5 3

C. Opposite of less m o r e
55 23 21 17

D. Citrus fruit that's green L i m e
9 45 24 43

E. Strength (rhymes with tower) P o w e r
25 19 1 34 40

F. Sing without moving your lips h u m
6 26 57

G. The price of an item c o s t
37 7 54 14

H. Baby cat K I t t e n
16 52 30 27 50 4

I. Dirty (rhymes with rusty) m u s t y
35 8 51 32 18

J. A 24-hour period D a y
10 15 60

K. A 60-minute period h o u r
33 48 13 59

L. Plaything t o y
53 39 11

M. Material that comes from sheep w o o l
41 12 31 47

N. A place where campers sleep t e n t
38 28 44 46

Answer:

w h e n   s h o u l d   y o u   t a k e
1 2 3 4   5 6 7 8 9 10   11 12 13   14 15 16 17

y o u r   c o m p u t e r   t o   t h e
18 19 20 21   22 23 24 25 26 27 28 29   30 31   32 33 34

m o _ t _ r ?   _ h e _   i _   _ _ s _ _
35 36 37 38 39 40   41 42 43 44   45 46   47 48 49 50 51

_ _ _   m e m o _ _ .
52 53 54   55 56 57 58 59 60

Answers on page 167.

SPEECHLESS

The start of President Lincoln's famous Gettysburg Address was faxed to us, but the machine was on the blink and cut out many of the words. Can you reconstruct the speech by placing each removed word into its correct spot below?

AL	AN	ATE	BERT	CORE	EAR
EAT	EVEN	FORT	GO	HAT	HE
HIS	ME	NAT	ONCE	OUGHT	OUR
POSITION	THE	TINE			

F_OUR_S_CORE_ A_N_D S_EVEN_
Y_EAR_S A_GO_, OUR FA_THE_RS
BR_OUGHT_ _FORT_H ON
T_HAT_ CON_TINE_NT A NEW
_NAT_ION, C_ONCE_IVED IN
LI_BERT_Y AND DEDIC_EAR_D
TO T_HE_ PRO_POSITION_
T_HAT_ ALL _ME_N ARE
CR_EATE_D EQU_AL_.

Answers on page 164.

ANIMUZZLE

Each animal in the list will fit into one spot in the diagram. Using the letters that are already in the grid to guide you, place each animal in the one place it fits.

3 Letters
ASS
CAT
ELK
EWE
GNU
HOG

4 Letters
GOAT
HARE

5 Letters
BISON
CAMEL
HORSE
HYENA
KOALA
SHEEP
SWINE
TIGER

6 Letters
COYOTE
ERMINE
FERRET
GERBIL
RABBIT

7 Letters
CHEETAH
GIRAFFE
HAMSTER
LEOPARD
RACCOON

8 Letters
ANTELOPE
SQUIRREL

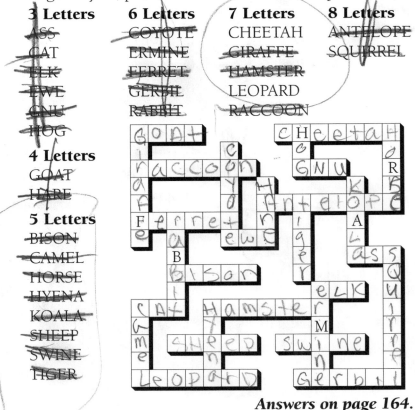

Answers on page 164.

END OF THE LINE

On each line below, add a letter to the word given at the left to make the word described in the parentheses ( ). Then, read *down* the column to answer this riddle: What is in the center of America and Australia?

P A R **T** (section)

M A R S **h** (swamp)

M A N **e** (lion's hair)

G R A V E **l** (tiny pebbles)

T O T **e** (large bag)

R A B B I **t** (hopping animal)

P A I N **t** (do artwork)

G R I M **e** (dirt)

M A Y O **r** (head of a city)

C O N D O **r** (large bird)

Answers on page 170.

ANSWERS

Eagle Eyes

Answer: Root beer

All Wet

S **t** rait
H arbor
Oc **e** an

Lak **e**
Cre **e** k
St **r** eam
I nlet
Chann **e** l

C ove
Se **a**
Po **n** d
B **a** y
Poo **l**

Answer: The Eerie (Erie) Canal

Blankety Blank

Bird **h** ouse
Cubb **y** hole
Quot **a** tion
Shor **t** cake
Race **t** rack

Litt **e** rbug
Nect **a** rine
Pape **r** back
Head **p** hone

Answer: Hyatt Earp

Monkey in the Middle

1. Bag	8. Light
2. Ball	9. Neck
3. Bill	10. Pan
4. Button	11. Stick
5. Check	12. Tooth
6. Cross	13. Water
7. Horse	14. Yard

Isle Aisle

Bu **n** ch
Sc **a** rf
Hi **n** ge
Ba **t** he
Sk **u** nk
Lu **c** ky
Jo **k** er
Sw **e** at
Me **t** er

Answer: Nantucket

Number Fun

Time
60 seconds in a minute
60 minutes in an hour
24 hours in a day
7 days in a week
31 days in a month except for
    February, April, June,
    September, and November
365 days in a year
10 years in a decade
4 seasons in a year

Literature
Snow White and the 7 Dwarfs
Goldilocks and the 3 Bears
The 3 Little Pigs

Money
100 pennies in a dollar
20 nickels in a dollar
10 dimes in a dollar
4 quarters in a dollar
2 half dollars in a dollar

History and Government
13 original colonies
9 justices on the Supreme
    Court
2 senators from each state

Sports
9 innings in a baseball game
18 holes on a golf course

Weights and Measures
12 inches in a foot
16 ounces in a pound

Transportation
4 wheels on a car
2 wheels on a bicycle

Science
9 planets in the solar system

Close Relatives
1. Vehicles Car
          Van
          Cab
2. Things to Read Novel
              Story
              Fairy tale
3. Desserts Pudding
            Pie
            Cookies
4. Females Girl
           Lady
           Woman
5. Languages German
             French
             Greek

6. Furniture Desk
Sofa
Table

7. U.S. Presidents Carter
Grant
Bush

8. Males Boy
Lad
Fellow

9. Reporters' Questions
Where?
When?
Why?

10. Fowl Chicken
Hen
Rooster

11. Colors Red
White
Blue

12. Animal Sounds Bark
Oink
Moo

13. Board Games Chess
Scrabble
Clue

14. States New York
Iowa
Ohio

Found Letters

Latter	S	Startle
Parent	T	Pattern
Space	E	Escape
Tureen	V	Venture
Rapper	E	Prepare
Agreed	N	Angered
Client	S	Stencil
Suet	Q	Quest
Sandy	U	Sunday
Verse	E	Severe
Hornet	A	Another
Wives	L	Swivel
Early	B	Barley
Their	E	Either
Impose	R	Promise
Leaner	G	Enlarge

Answer: Steven Squealberg

Express Yourself

1. Long underwear
2. Up a creek
3. Downtown
4. "Malcolm in the Middle"
5. *Little Women*
6. Big shot
7. Six of one; half a dozen of the other

8. Back stroke
9. Scrambled eggs
10. Long Island
11. Reading between the lines
12. Five pounds overweight
13. Two-way street
14. Broken hearted
15. The day after tomorrow

So Symbol

1. Ca**nine**
2. Ca**t**alog
3. **Check**ers
4. **Dash**ing
5. **Equal**ity
6. H**and**some
7. Per**cent**age
8. Sp**arrow**
9. **Start**led
10. Sur**plus**
11. Teleph**one**
12. **Ten**ants
13. **W**e**ight**lifter

Speechless

F**our**score **and** s**even** y**ears** a**go**, our fa**the**rs br**ought** for**th** on **this** contin**en**t a new **nat**ion, c**once**ived in Li**berty**, and dedic**ate**d to t**he** pro**position** t**hat** all **me**n are crea**te**d equ**al**.

Gridlock

```
C S R C L S     L R S L W B
O T A R U H     O A L A A R
MONACO          ODESSA
M R G Z K R     S A E S T V
A K E Y Y E     E R T O E E

S P B G L C     T S B H Q F
H U A U O H     U T A U U U
OTTAWA          MADRID
V T C V E M     M R G R T G
E Y H A R P     Y K E Y E E

L E F B B M     S W P B G S
E Q U A R O     H A U R I
MUSCAT          LONDON
O A S O K T     L L I D W C
N L Y N E O     Y E C Y L E
```

Animuzzle

Opposite Distraction

1. Closet	16. Curfew
2. Copenhagen	17. Below
3. Puppet	18. Prolong
4. Thinkers	19. Tango
5. Mouth	20. Explain
6. Blunder	21. Prefix
7. Colder	22. Pasture
8. Coffin	23. Overtake
9. Meander	24. Deposit
10. Lightning	25. Washout
11. Turban	26. Scared
12. Pleasure	27. Disappear
13. Plates	28. Frigid
14. Ladder	29. Offensive
15. Greasy	30. Passenger

Mini Fill-ins

Sports

Drinks

Cheeses

Dances

Filling Station

1, 2, 3 = Hid
4, 5, 6 = Her
7, 8, 9 = All
10, 11, 12, 13 = Over
14, 15, 16, 17 = Life
18, 19, 20, 21, 22 = Teeth
23, 24, 25 = Wet

Why did the ram fall over a cliff? He didn't see the ewe turn.

Fabric-ation

The following fabrics are crossed out (in order):

Felt	Silk
Flannel	Chintz
Corduroy	Denim
Wool	Organdy
Cashmere	Orlon
Velvet	Linen
Suede	Taffeta
Rayon	Chenille
Cotton	Cheesecloth
Nylon	Seersucker

Riddle answer: He is fully recovered.

One from Column A

1. Cap/a/city
2. Car/am/el
3. Char/it/able
4. Drag/on/fly
5. For/bid/den
6. Gig/an/tic
7. Marsh/mall/ow
8. Pen/man/ship
9. Pep/per/mint
10. Therm/o/meter

Man, Oh, Man!

1. Commander
2. Fireman
3. Germany
4. Katmandu
5. Manager
6. Mango
7. Manhattan
8. Manhunt
9. Maniac
10. Manicure
11. Manila
12. Mansion
13. Manual
14. Truman
15. Woman

Peo/ple/asers

1. Alec Baldwin/winter
2. Andre Braugher/heroine
3. Benjamin Bratt/attack
4. Bill Clinton/tonight
5. Billy Crudup/duplicate
6. Brendan Fraser/servant

7. Calista Flockhart/artist
8. Christina Aguilera/eraser
9. Claire Danes/nestled
10. Derek Jeter/terminal
11. Donald Trump/umpire
12. Geena Davis/visitor
13. Harrison Ford/ordinary
14. Heather Locklear/early
15. Helen Hunt/until

Low Tech

A. Usher
B. Choose
C. More
D. Lime
E. Power
F. Hum
G. Cost
H. Kitten
I. Dusty
J. Day
K. Hour
L. Toy
M. Wool
N. Tent

Answer: When should you take your computer to the doctor? When it loses its memory.

Bird Watching

1. H<u>OW L</u>OVELY YOU LOOK!
2. PLEASE SEN<u>D OVER</u> THAT PICTURE.
3. THE SHIP'S <u>SPAR ROT</u>ATED EASILY.
4. THAT FELLO<u>W REN</u>TED A CAR.
5. THEY FOUND THE L<u>OST RICH</u>ES.
6. DRIVE FA<u>ST OR K</u>EEP TO THE RIGHT.
7. SAY HE<u>LLO ON</u>CE MORE.
8. GIVE ME A DOL<u>LAR K</u>ELLY.
9. HERE'S THE <u>CHAPEL I CAN</u> ATTEND.
10. A FABRIC LIKE LY<u>CRA NE</u>EDS VERY LITTLE CARE.
11. <u>CAN A RYE</u> BREAD BE MADE AT HOME?
12. PUT YOUR BUSINESS <u>CARD IN AL</u>BERT'S HAND.
13. SHE' <u>S WAN</u>DERING AWAY.
14. THEY C<u>RAVE N</u>EW FOODS.
15. DRINK THE T<u>EA GLEN</u>DA BROUGHT.

16. HE GREW ONE HAL<u>F INCH</u>.
17. THE CHE<u>F AL CON</u>TACTED IS COOKING DINNER.
18. UNT<u>HAW KIM</u>'S SUPPER.

Pop Stars

1. Brad Pitt
2. Britney Spears
3. Dixie Chicks
4. Drew Barrymore
5. Jim Carrey
6. Keri Russell
7. Mick Jagger
8. Ricky Martin
9. Spice Girls
10. Will Smith

Cosmetic Surgery

1. Cats
2. Cheaters
3. Defeat
4. Earthquake
5. Edison
6. Forecast
7. Garments
8. Gobbles
9. Israel
10. Legends

Just the Same

1. **Amaze**ment
2. B**aloney**
3. B**raid**
4. **Brain**storm
5. Cal**end**ar
6. **Charm**ing
7. **Chill**y
8. Cou**rage**
9. De**crease**
10. Dis**cover**
11. D**rawer**
12. **Fat**igue
13. For**get**
14. Fr**owned**
15. **Mat**tress
16. **Mist**ake
17. No**mad**
18. Ost**rich**
19. **Pal**ace
20. Pan**try**
21. **Phot**ograph
22. P**roverb**
23. Qu**easy**
24. Rest**less**
25. Sc**all**ops
26. S**carce**
27. S**wee**t
28. S**win**dle
29. **Trip**od
30. **Yell**ow

Changeover #1

1. Flea
2. Able
3. Sour
4. Hint
5. Idea
6. Once
7. Note
8. Sole

Answer: Fashions

1. Skis
2. Eager
3. Aches
4. Shot
5. Ocean
6. Night
7. Stove

Answer: Seasons

Partners

1. Mom & Dad
2. Pork & beans
3. Coffee & cream
4. Horse & carriage
5. Car & driver
6. Table & chairs
7. Boy & girl
8. Snow & sleet
9. Pail & shovel
10. Shirt & tie
11. Rod & reel
12. Shoes & socks
13. Milk & cookies
14. Bacon & eggs
15. Bride & groom

Top Guy

Answer: Zachary Taylor

Anna's Gram
4-Letter Words

1. Boss/sobs
2. Care/race
3. Pals/slap
4. Part/trap
5. Grin/ring
6. None/neon
7. Leak/lake
8. Late/tale
9. Calm/clam

End/Start

1. Acrobat/battery
2. Babysit/situate
3. Bayonet/network
4. Benefit/fitness
5. Butcher/heroine
6. Catalog/logical
7. Cookout/outside
8. Distant/antonym
9. Frantic/tickled
10. Garbage/agendas
11. Illegal/gallery
12. Justice/iceberg
13. Kneepad/paddled
14. Opossum/summary
15. Postman/manhole
16. Pumpkin/kingdom
17. Showoff/officer
18. Skipper/perfume
19. Taxicab/cabinet
20. Tornado/adopted

Daffynitions

1. E	6. G	11. J
2. I	7. N	12. H
3. L	8. B	13. O
4. K	9. D	14. F
5. M	10. C	15. A

Name That Word

1. Banner	9. Destroy
2. Beagle	10. Enjoyment
3. Beneath	11. Evaporate
4. Calculator	12. Formal
5. Cartoon	13. Giant
6. Creamy	14. Idolize
7. Dangerous	15. President
8. Delightful	16. Stomach

Changeover #2

1. Bagel	6. Ride
2. Acted	7. Itch
3. Throw	8. Easel
4. These	9. Sword
5. Earth	

Answer: Batteries

1. Odor	5. Iced
2. Plum	6. Over
3. Inch	7. Nuts
4. Near	8. Skis

Answer: Opinions

Cross-Offs

A. Bunny, kitten, joey, puppy
B. Trace, caret, crate, react
C. Sacramento, Oakland, Pasadena, Fresno
D. Candy, chips, pretzels
E. West, South, East, North
F. Clerk, receptionist
G. Christmas, Kwanza, Hanukkah

Leftover words: NOW GO BELL PIPE FROG WRING.
Riddle answer: HOW TO TELL RIPE FROM WRONG.

End of the Line

Par **t**
Mars **h**
Man **e**

Grave **l**
Tot **e**
Rabbi **t**
Pain **t**
Grim **e**
Mayo **r**

Condo **r**

Answer: The letter R

MIND BOGGLERS

MIND BOGGLER

Here's a quick brainteaser: What is special about the
grid below—and what is missing from it?

Answer on page 271.

U	R	O	W
O	N	G	T
F	I	E	H
X	V	S	R

TYING THE KNOT

According to an ancient custom, if a woman throws five ropes out of a high window, and three or more of them land such that they will form knots when both ends are pulled, she will be married within the next year.

The ropes here show one woman's tosses. Should she expect a wedding this year?

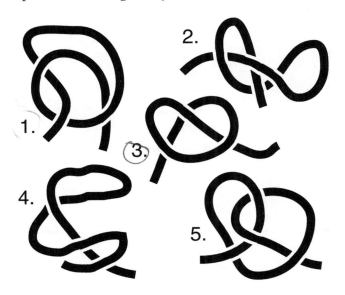

Answer on page 279.

TECHNIQUE-COLOR

Jo is making a stained-glass window, and she wants each adjacent piece of glass to be a different color. She wants to use just four colors: yellow, orange, purple, and red.

If the center circle is yellow, and two other pieces are colored as shown, what color does piece A need to be?

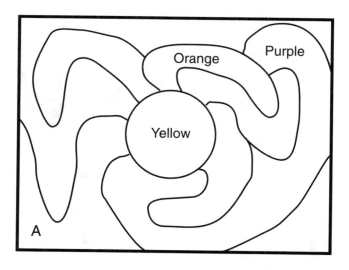

Answer on page 278.

ANIMAL STRENGTH

If the first two tug of war contests shown here are ties, which group will win the third contest, or will it also be a draw?

$$3F = 2S$$
$$4S = 3T$$

Answer on page 260.

THEORY OF RELATIVITY

At the Embee family reunion, your sister is talking to your grandmother Mary, your cousin Bo, and your uncle Bill. Who are you?

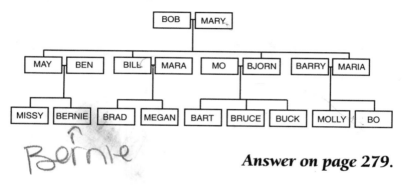

Bernie

Answer on page 279.

PRODUCE PRODUCTS

The numbers one through nine are represented by nine different vegetables in the equations below. Each veggie represents the same number throughout. If the broccoli equals three, what is the identity of the carrot?

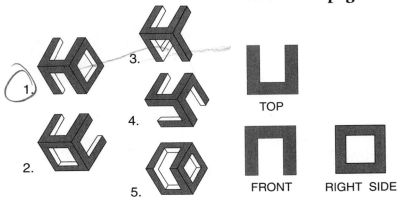

Answer on page 274.

WHAT'S THE PLAN?

Which three-dimensional object on the left does the simple orthographic projection on the right represent?

Answer on page 280.

PAPER CLIP FLIP

Most of the wire sculptures below were made from
standard paper clips, by twisting them at existing bends.

Which of the shapes could not have been made by
bending the original paper clip?

Answer on page 273.

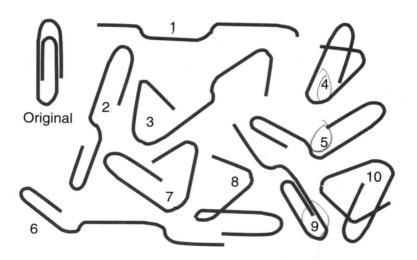

12-STEP PROGRAM

Work through the code of this computer program, line by line. Your output will answer this riddle: WHAT DID COWBOY DAVE HAVE TO DO BEFORE GOING TO THE COMPUTER-USERS' DANCE?

01 Set Number = 1
02 Set Letter at (Number) = "P"
03 Number = Number + 3
04 Set Letter at (Number) = "O"
05 Number = Number + 1
06 If Number £5 go to line 04
07 Set Letter at (Number) = "B"
08 Number = Number ÷ 3
09 Set Letter at (Number) = "U"
10 Number = Number + 1
11 Set Letter at (Number) = "T"
12 Reverse the output

Output:

$$\overline{\quad} \quad \overline{\quad} \quad \overline{\quad} \quad \overline{\quad} \quad \overline{\quad} \quad \overline{\quad}$$
1   2   3   4   5   6

Answer on page 279.

THIRTEEN CANDLES

Claude doesn't want anyone to know how old he is unless they do some work. So he designed a birthday cake that uses 13 candles and represents his age.

If you count all of the triangles of all sizes formed by the lines connecting the candles, you will discover Claude's age. Can you figure it out before the candles are blown out?

Answer on page 279.

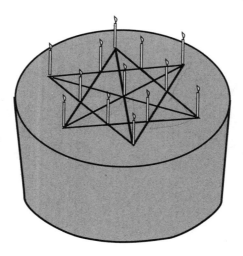

HAIRY TALES

1. Rapunzel's hair grew 100 feet longer while waiting to be saved by the prince. Hair grows one inch every two months. So, how long had the fair maiden been trapped in the tower when she was rescued?

2. In Washington Irving's story, Rip Van Winkle's beard grew two feet in the 20 years that he slept. Is the story accurate?

Answer on page 267.

KEEP THE FAITH

The eruptions of the Old Faithful geyser are indeed very predictable. Below are the last five eruptions:

1. at 12:00 P.M. for five minutes
2. at 12:50 P.M. for six minutes
3. at 1:44 P.M. for seven minutes
4. at 2:42 P.M. for eight minutes
5. at 3:44 P.M. for nine minutes

Can you calculate when the next eruption will be?

Answer on page 269.

BLOCK PARTY

The alphabet blocks below are of two different types, turned around in various positions. No letter appears on both types of block. The letters on the underside of the blocks spell out the answer to this riddle:

HOW DID BARBIE GET THROUGH THE PILE OF ALPHABET BLOCKS?

Can you do some mental tumbling and figure out the solution?

Answer on page 261.

She took the . . .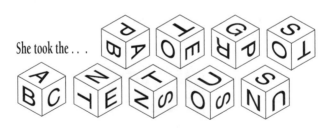

SELF TEST

The answers to the questions on the following page are one-digit numbers from one to nine, and no number is repeated.

Can you figure out the unique set of answers?

1. Answer to statement 5 minus answer to statement 4.
2. Answer to statement 8 times answer to statement 9.
3. Answer to statement 4 plus answer to statement 8.
4. Number of times that the number 9 is an answer.
5. Total number of statements.
6. Answer to statement 1 minus answer to statement 4.
7. Number of odd answers.
8. Answer to statement 2 divided by answer to statement 9.
9. Answer to statement 6 minus answer to statement 7.

Answer on page 276.

LOSING TRACK

On this animal track quiz, one student copied his or her answers from the other three students. By looking at their answers below, you should be able to tell who cheated.

Ironically, the cheater got none of the answers correct. If the other students had two correct answers each, what are the correct answers?

The Question:
Match these five tracks to the animals that made them.

The Answers:
ART: 1. deer 2. caribou 3. mt. goat 4. moose 5. bison
BOB: 1. caribou 2. moose 3. deer 4. bison 5. mt. goat
CAT: 1. bison 2. mt. goat 3. deer 4. caribou 5. moose
DEB: 1. deer 2. moose 3. mt. goat 4. caribou 5. bison

Answer on page 270.

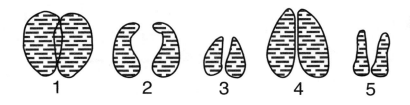

BLIND ALLEYS

On his birthday, Joe's friends blindfolded him and took him for a drive.

If they took two right turns, a left turn, and another left, and ended up at Wally World, where did they start?

Answer on page 261.

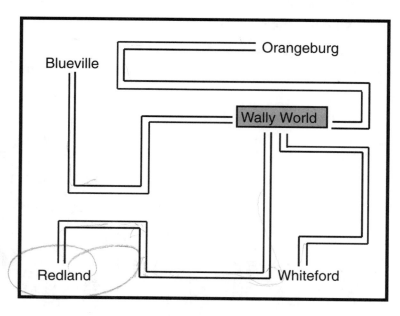

GRAPHIC LANGUAGE

Find the letters that correspond to the coordinates given below. Write them in order on the dashes to answer this riddle: WHY WAS SIX AFRAID OF SEVEN?

1. C5
2. G3
3. A3
4. D5
5. F2
6. A1
7. D2
8. F4
9. B4
10. E6
11. B6
12. C3
13. A5
14. E1

	A	B	C	D	E	F	G
6	D	N	R	Y	T	M	F
5	N	L	S	E	O	K	Z
4	P	H	J	C	B	G	A
3	V	O	I	R	U	W	E
2	U	M	X	I	T	N	P
1	E	A	G	Q	E	S	L

Answer:

BECAUSE $\underline{seven\ eight\ nine}$.

Answer on page 267.

FRACTION WORDS

Add the parts of words below as indicated to come up with two answer words. In each case, use the first letters of the word in your addition. For example, one-third of CAT would be C.

Both solutions answer this riddle: What has keys, but can't open a door?

Answer on page 265.

A.

$\frac{2}{3}$ $+\frac{1}{3}$ $+\frac{3}{5}$

B.

$\frac{2}{3}$ $+\frac{2}{3}$ $+\frac{1}{7}$

THREE HEXES

Most of the shapes here can be made by combining three equal-sized hexagons. Which ones cannot?

Answer on page 279.

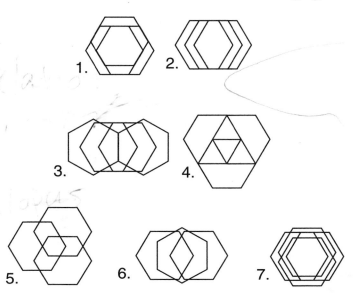

TEN GOLD COINS

Ten gold coins are hidden under ten of the unlabeled hexagonal tiles in this floor. The numbers on the labeled tiles indicate how many coins are under tiles adjacent to that tile.

Can you locate the ten gold coins without looking under any of the wrong tiles?

Answer on page 278.

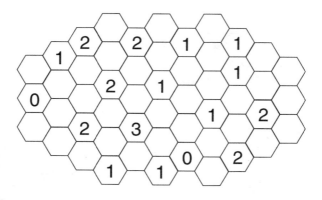

MIRROR IMAGES

Using only a square mirror and the jigsaw shape below, most of the figures below can be formed. Which figures are impossible? (Remember, parts of the new shapes are seen in the mirror.)

Answer on page 271.

WINTER EYES

To make simple snowflakes, fold a square of paper into quarters, cut shapes, and unfold. Which folded snowflakes (1–7) will unfold to create snowflakes A, B, and C?

Answer on page 280.

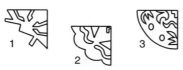

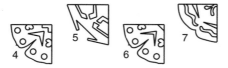

FISHING FOR WORDS

Remove words from the nonsense paragraph below as instructed. When you are done, the words that remain will spell out a Spanish proverb.

THOUGH FEROCIOUS THE GREEN TURTLE SPIT LOWER FISH STRESSED BARREL DIES GULP BECAUSE HE EAR CANNOT PLUG OPENS RIGHT INK HIS TEN WHISTLING TIPS SHARKS NET MOUTH LAKE DESSERTS.

1. Remove all of the words that are between two words that begin with a T.

2. Take away all of the pairs of words that spell each other backward.

3. Cross out all of the words that become another word when an F is added before the first letter.

4. Remove all of the six-letter words.

Answer on page 264.

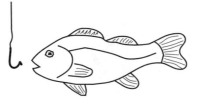

GOT CLASS?

It's time to put together your class schedule for next semester's classes. You need to take two science classes, one math or computer class, one English class, and one history. Given the list of classes that sound interesting to you, which combination of class times will work? (R is Thursday.)

American history	TRF 9:05-10:00
Biology	TR 8:00-10:00
Calculus	MW 11:15-1:15
English lit	TR 9:05-10:00
European history	MWF 10:10-11:05
Genetics	MWF 12:20-1:15
PC basics	TR 12:20-1:15
Physics	MWF 10:10-11:05
Shakespeare	TR 11:15-1:15
Statistics	MWF 8:00-9:10

Answer on page 267.

NEXT IN LINE

The four pictures below form a logical sequence in order from left to right. Can you figure out what links one picture to the next and then deduce which of the three objects (a, b, or c) below comes next in the line?

Answer on page 271.

1.   2.   3.   4.

a.

b.

c.

FISHING LINES

Today, eight people are trying to hook some trout on this part of the Lazy River.

Fishermen like to fish their own holes. To separate everyone, draw two straight lines across the map so that each fisher is on his or her own piece of river. Can you find a way for Mac to fish on his own piece of river? What about Bill?

Answer on page 264.

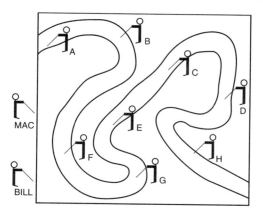

A GOOD EGG

Ostriches lay the largest eggs in the world. To find out how many omelets can be made from one ostrich egg, solve the word puzzle below. (Each omelet uses the equivalent of two hen's eggs.)

Spell the six-letter answer as described:

1. A letter in EGRET but not GREBE
2. A letter in CROW but not CONDOR
3. A letter in WARBLER but not BARN OWL
4. A letter in KESTREL, EAGLE, and FALCON
5. A letter in RAVEN but not CRANE
6. A letter in PIGEON, WREN, and OSPREY

— — — — — —

Answer on page 266.

SEA OR SOIL?

The good news is that your rich uncle Charlie has bequeathed to you a treasure map. The bad news is that it has been ripped on all four sides, so that you have only the key piece.

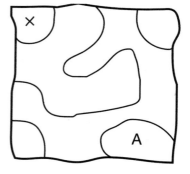

You are told that there is a treasure buried at point X and that point A is on land. If the area is composed of one lake and the land around it, and there are no islands in the lake, is the treasure undersea or under land?

Answer on page 275.

BERRY IMPRESSIVE

A new, genetically engineered strawberry clones itself every month, except for the first month, when it is dormant. Each new strawberry is identical to the first one in that it, too, clones itself every month after being dormant for a month. If one of these new strawberries is

planted at the beginning of March and harvested at the beginning of November, how many berries will result?

Answer on page 260.

MATCH BOXES

Which pieces of cardboard below will form boxes if they are folded along the lines?

Answer on page 270.

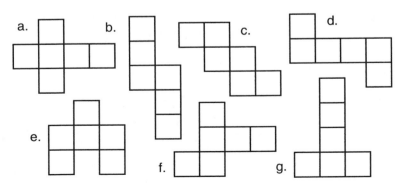

AGES OF REASON

Aunt Pearl doesn't like to tell anyone her age, but she will say this:

"In Roman numerals, my age is made up of one I, one V, one L, and one X. My age is the second largest number that can be made from those symbols. My daughter's age is the second smallest number that can be made from those symbols."

How old is Pearl and how old is your cousin?

HAPPY BIRTHDAY

To a favorite aunt

Answer on page 260.

JOLLOS AND PLOTZ

These are jollos:

These are plotz:

Which are jollos and which are plotz?

A. B. C. D. E.

Answer on page 268.

SLICE OF LIFE

Your meatball pizza just came out of the oven and now you need to feed six hungry kids. These kids are picky,

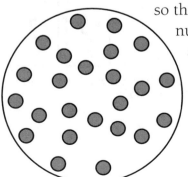

so they each want the same number of meatballs. They also each want the same size piece of pizza. How can you cut the pie to satisfy all six kids?

Answer on page 276.

BLACK AND WHITE

In this game, you can see your friends' cards, but not your own. If there are four black cards and four white cards to choose from, can you deduce which cards you have by what the other players know?

Answer on page 261.

1.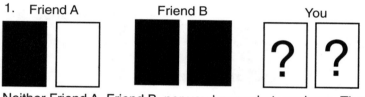

Neither Friend A, Friend B, nor you know what you have. Then, friend A says she knows. What cards do you have?

2.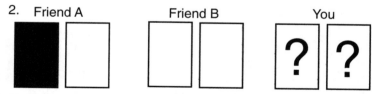

Neither Friend A, Friend B, or you know what you have. Then, Friend A still doesn't know. What cards do you have?

FOR YOUR THOUGHTS

1. Which circle below is the size of a penny?

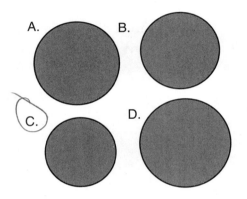

2. How many pennies, stacked on their sides, equal the diameter of one penny?

   A. eight B. ten C. twelve D. fourteen

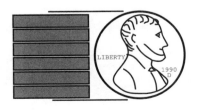

Answers on page 265.

GAME PLAN

In these super tic-tac-toe games, the letters are entered from the top of the board, so that only the lowest empty box in each column can be played. If it's O's turn in game A and X's turn in game B, who should win each game? (Three X's or O's in a row wins.)

Answers on page 265.

A.

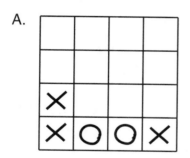

B.

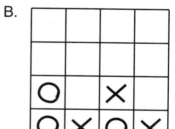

RUFF AND READY

At the recent running of the Doggie Jog, every person ran with at least one dog.
The organizers
want to know
how many dogs

and people participated. Unfortunately, the clumsy photographer tripped as he took the group picture, and got a shot of the racers' feet, but nothing else. A reporter in a helicopter scanned the canines and humans from above, but his scanner picked up only the total number of eyes. If the photographer counted 196 feet and paws and the reporter tallied 126 eyes, how many people and how many dogs ran the race?

Answer on page 275.

SHIFTING GEARS

In each case, which way will gear C turn?

Answers on page 276.

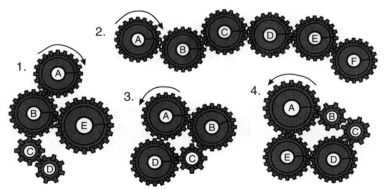

IRISH EYES

Can you find the four-leaf clover in this field? Good luck!

Answer on page 268.

TO THE LETTER

All of the eight shapes on the next page are parts of the 26 letters shown to the left of them, although they may have been enlarged and rotated. Figure out which letter

each shape was taken from. The answers, in order, will
spell a word.

Answers on page 279.

abcdefghij
klmnopqr
stuvwxyz

KEY RINGS

In each group below, if any one of the rings were
picked up, would all of the other rings be lifted with it?

Answers on page 269.

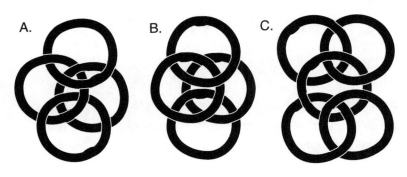

IT'S ABOUT TIME

Match each definition to a clock shown at right.

1. Snack time
2. Work time
3. Flight time
4. Tax time
5. Height time
6. Class time

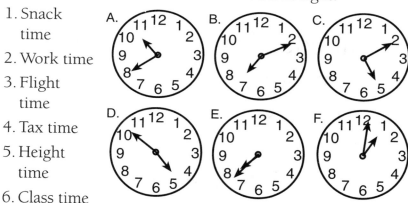

Answer on page 268.

DETECTIVE STORY

"Detective Slooth? This is Sergeant Chiller from Thunder Bay. We have been tracking a jewelry thief and he's headed south toward you. He is driving a red Honda Civic above the speed limit and he's dressed for the weather, which is 30 degrees. I hope you can help

us intercept him before he pawns off the goods."

   Detective Slooth sees a red Honda Civic coming into Duluth, but the driver is wearing shorts and a tank top. What should he do?

Answer on page 263.

FAMILIAR FACES

Which of these familiar faces are facing the correct way, and which are mirror images?

Answer on page 264.

COFFEE BREAK

Sally decided she wanted to give up coffee. She thought she would drink tea instead, until she read that one pound of black tea  contains twice as much caffeine as one pound of coffee.

However, Sally should also know that one pound of tea yields about 160 cups, whereas one pound of coffee makes about 40 cups. One 12-ounce can of cola  has about one-quarter of the caffeine as a cup of coffee.

How much caffeine is in a cup of tea, relative to a cup of coffee and to a can of cola?

Answer on page 262.

TOUGH COOKIES

Joey's mom brought out a plate of cookies for him and four friends. Unfortunately, there was one cookie too many to divide them evenly. Then, Ben came in and they figured that each of them could get the same number of cookies. The kids were just about to eat when Sarah came through the door. Sadly, the cookies could not be divided evenly any more. But Joey pointed out that if they gave one to his mom, the rest would divide evenly. How many cookies were on the plate? (Hint: There were fewer than 100.)

Answer on page 279.

BEADY EYES

What number was added to the number on abacus A to get the total shown on abacus B?

Answer on page 260.

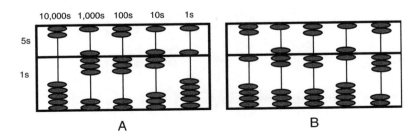

A   B

PAPER PINBALL

Begin at IN (10 points) and move along the lines to
OUT (5 points), calculating as you go to get a high
score. You may hit the same bumper twice, but you
may not trace over any part of your path. Our high
score is 295. Can you beat it?

Answer on page 273.

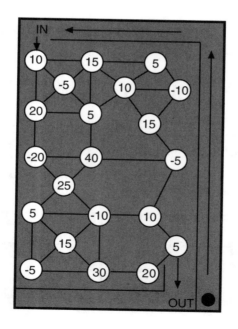

GET THE SCOOP

Ken and Terry's, the local ice cream shop, will be giving away free cones some time this year. Because they want to limit the lines a bit, they have given out three clues as to the date of their giveaway. Can you figure out when it will be?

- The giveaway will be in the first week of a month without an A in it.

- It will be on a day of the week that has a U in it.

- The month has no E but the day of the week contains an E.

Answer on page 265.

CATEGORICALLY SPEAKING

The 25 words below are the answers to a game of Categories. That is, each of them fits one of five categories and begins with one of five letters. Can you reconstruct the categories and arrange the words so that each category contains a word beginning with each letter?

Answer on page 262.

MAGENTA CORAL   MANGO

AMETHYST SHELL CHESTNUT

SNOWBALL PURPLE MUSSEL

CANDY CAMELLIA SPRUCE

ANEMONE MAGNOLIA   PAIL

PALM SAND SCARLET CHAIR

MYRTLE AMARYLLIS APPLE

PEARL PRIMROSE AMBER

FIT FOR A PRINCESS

Young Princess Figleaf of Lalaland has four pieces of jewelry that are family heirlooms: a necklace, a ring, a bracelet, and a brooch. Being a fashion-conscious noble, she doesn't like to wear the same thing twice.

How many different combinations of crown jewels can Princess Figleaf wear? She may wear any number of jewels at a time.

Answer on page 265.

GLOBAL ECONOMY

While on a round-the-world trip, Wally priced the new
Whales CD in eight countries. In which country
should he buy the CD to get the best deal?

COST OF CD
Here's what the CD costs
in each country:

90 francs
1,265 yen
420 rupee
70.2 krona
18.2 Canadian dollars
17,000 lira
158 pesos
59.4 Egyptian pounds

EXCHANGE RATES
One American dollar buys:

1.3 Canadian dollars
6.0 French francs
1,700 Italian lira
7.8 Swedish krona
7.9 Mexican pesos
3.3 Egyptian pounds
35 Indian rupees
115 Japanese yen

Answer on page 266.

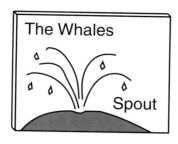

NOVEL IDEA

Follow the directions here very carefully, and you will find a humorous ending to this sentence starter:
AUTHORS ARE ALL . . .

1. Take out all the spaces, and remove the O.

2. Replace the two-letter postal code for a western state with a W.

3. Add two Ds at the very end.

4. Add "THE" between the E and the A.

5. Add an N between any repeated letters.

6. Add an I before the second A and a T after the A.

7. Add the word ME before the last two letters.

8. Delete every odd letter (the first, third, etc.).

9. Add a space and read the answer.

Answer on page 271.

ALLIGATOR ALLY

Use logic to figure out which is the alligator and which is the crocodile. One of them is telling the truth and one is lying.

Answer on page 260.

GIVE ME FIVE

Believe it or not, five twos equal five. So do five threes. And five fours.

Insert symbols for addition, subtraction, multiplication, and division into the formulas below to make each equation true. You may also use parentheses. The first equation is filled in for you.

$$(2 \times 2 \times 2 + 2) \div 2 = 5$$

3   3   3   3   3 = 5

4   4   4   4   4 = 5

5   5   5   5   5 = 5

6   6   6   6   6 = 5

7   7   7   7   7 = 5

8   8   8   8   8 = 5

9   9   9   9   9 = 5

Answer on page 266.

HULA HOOPLA

The simple arithmetic problems below are spelled out in Hawaiian. If all of the words represent one-digit numbers and are not zero or one, can you figure out the solution to the last equation?

HAWAIIAN EQUATIONS:

1. e'lua × e'lua + e'lima = e'iwa
2. e'walu ÷ e'ha × e'lua = e'ha
3. e'iwa ÷ e'kolu + e'kolu = e'ono
4. e'lua + e'ono − e'kolu = ??

Answer on page 268.

STRIKE IT, RICH

Last Sunday, Rich bowled an almost perfect game. His friend Carl noticed that he knocked over the same number of pins as Rich but didn't score nearly as well. What are the two most divergent scores that can be bowled by knocking over the same number of pins?

Answer on page 277.

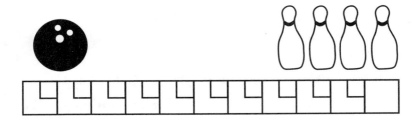

RUNED PUNCH LINE

Can you decipher this joke and its punch line, which are written in a runic alphabet?

Answer on page 275.

Hint: The first three words (which are shown below) are, WHAT DID THE . . .

PIE-EYED

Grandma said she'd make her homemade cherry pie if you can figure out this problem: Given three bowls and 12 cherries, can you arrange the fruit so that there are an odd number of cherries in each bowl? Oh, and each bowl must contain more than three cherries.

Answer on page 273.

SECRET WORDS

The first secret word has exactly two letters that are in each of these words:

RIOT WRAP
CHEW RACK
COLD GOWN

Can you name the word?

The second secret word has exactly two letters that are in each of these words:

VIDEO   CURVY
NORTH   HONEY
SPARK   VALID

Can you name the second word?

Answer on page 276.

JUMPER CABLES

In gym class, the teacher told a group of kids to each grab a jump rope from a pile. Which two kids are holding the same rope?

Answer on page 269.

CATCH A CODE

Use the Morse code key to help you solve the coded message. The message is written without breaks between letters. When decoded, the dots and dashes will answer this question:

What did the code inventor think when he had to repeat his message three times?

A • –	N – •
B – • • •	O – – –
C – • – •	P • – – •
D – • •	Q – – • –
E •	R • – •
F • • – •	S • • •
G – – •	T –
H • • • •	U • • –
I • •	V • • • –
J • – – –	W • – –
K – • –	X – • • –
L • – • •	Y – • – –
M – –	Z – – • •

MESSAGE: • • • • • • _ • • • _ • • _
• _ • • _ _ _ _ _ • _ • • • • •

Answer on page 261.

OUT OF SHAPE

The original shape below can be flipped and rotated in many ways. Which of the figures is not a rotated (or flipped) version of the original shape?

Answer on page 273.

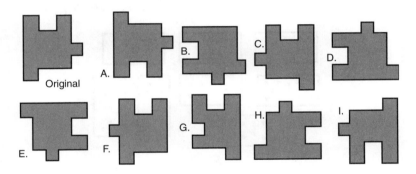

DOMINO EFFECT

Can you arrange the eight dominoes below to form a four-by-four square in which the number of pips in each row and column is the same? There is more than one answer.

Answer on page 263.

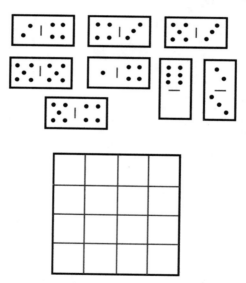

TALK FOR A SPELL

Eight businesses in Centerville have phone numbers that spell out words appropriate for their services. Using the telephone number key, can you match each phone number to the business that uses it and name the word or words that each phone number stands for?

a. 356-9377   Travel agent

b. 967-5688   Coffee shop

c. 424-7288   Florist

d. 359-2929   Barber

e. 468-5282   Costume shop

f. 373-7787   Bank

g. 738-2273   Veterinarian

h. 728-3669   Health club

1	2 ABC	3 DEF
4 GHI	5 JKL	6 MNO
7 PRS	8 TUV	9 WXY

Answer on page 278.

SYMBOL MAZE

To solve this maze, you may move from one box to another only if they share a symbol. You will not use any symbol more than once. You may not move to any box that adjoins the box you are in (even diagonally). Start in the upper left corner and try to visit each box exactly once.

Answer on page 278.

MATH MAZE

Begin with the number in the upper left square and travel to the lower right, calculating as you go. Can you find the solution path that meets the following restrictions?

- You may move to any adjacent (but not diagonal) square.
- You may not visit any square more than once.
- You must finish with the value shown in the last square.

Hint: No result along the way is a negative number or a fraction.

BEGIN

3	+4	ñ1	•4	˜5
•2	ñ5	•3	ñ8	ñ2
•0	•7	˜2	+6	˜3
˜5	x6	+1	•5	+2
+8	˜4	+7	ñ9	=9

END

Answer on page 270.

FIT TO BE TILED

Mrs. McGillicutty wants to put tile tops on two large tables. She wants to use tiles of either shape A or shape B. Each square in the tiles

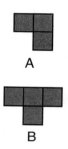

A

B

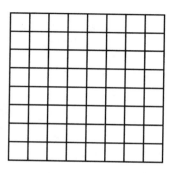

is one foot by one foot. The first table is eight by six feet and the second is eight by eight feet. Can you cover both tables according to her wishes without cutting any tiles?

Answer on page 265.

ZONED OUT

Amy is about to get on her flight to return home from Manila, and she wants to tell her boyfriend, Sheldon, when to pick her up at Kennedy airport. It is Thursday and her flight leaves at 4 P.M.

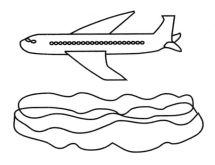

If New York is 11 hours behind the Philippines and Amy's flight time is 18 hours, plus an eight-hour layover in Hawaii, what day and time should Sheldon be waiting for her in New York?

Answer on page 280.

RECEIPT DECEIT

The cash register printout at the Deuce hardware store isn't working very well. It is printing two sales on top of one another.

If Hank knows that one of his items cost $3.25, can you deduce the cost of his other purchases, his tax, and his total bill? Also, what were the amounts in the sale before his?

3..25	
4..95	
1..64	
5..40	SUB
..25	TAX
5..55	TOT

Answer on page 275.

THE GREAT PUMPKIN

Tom asked his mom for a recipe for pumpkin pie, because she makes great pies for the Elk's Club every year. Unfortunately, his mother uses a recipe for 80 pies.

If Tom has the ingredients that are listed, does he have enough to make two pies, based on the amounts from his mother's recipe?

MOM'S RECIPE
140 cups pumpkin
10 dozen eggs
120 cups evaporated milk
60 cups sugar
80 tsp. cinnamon

TOM'S PANTRY
4 cups pumpkin
2 eggs
3 cups evaporated milk
2 cups sugar
2 tsp. cinnamon

Answer on page 267.

STARRY EYES

Can you find the one perfect, five-sided star in the field of shapes?

Answer on page 277.

DRAW BY NUMBERS

Connect the points in the graph as directed. When you're done, you should see a familiar object.

Go from C10 to B10 to D13 to G14 to M14 to P13 to R10 to Q10 to P11 to N8 to N6 to P7 to Q7 to O4 to L5 to H5 to D1 to D2 to A5 to B6 to C5 to E5 to F9 to D11 to C10.

Then go from G9 to M9 to O12 to L13 to G13 to E12 to G9.

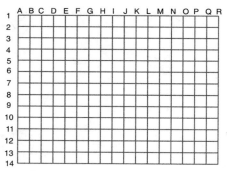

Answer on page 264.

THE PENNY FAIRY

Kelly rubbed her piggy bank and the Penny Fairy appeared. He told her she could choose her reward for freeing him. She could either have a ton of pennies or four miles of pennies lined up end to end. Which would you guess would be more money? Do some calculations to see if you are right.

Penny facts:

- One penny weighs about .0875 ounces.
- One penny is about .75 inches in diameter.

Answer on page 273.

PIECES OF WISDOM

If you can put these jigsaw pieces together mentally, you will find part of a quote from Ralph Waldo Emerson describing what it is to be successful.

Answer on page 273.

UNFOLDING MYSTERY

Two pieces of paper have been folded into fourths, and cut-outs have been made in them as shown (1 and 2). What will the unfolded pieces look like (a, b, c, d, e, or f)?

Answer on page 280.

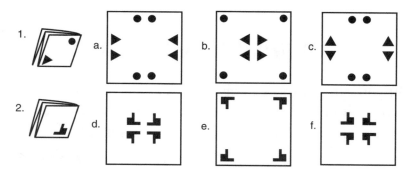

PUZZLE PUZZLE

Every year for her birthday, Sandy gets a square jigsaw puzzle from her uncle. Each year, he finds a puzzle with more pieces than the last. This year, she received a 2,025 piece puzzle. How many edge pieces (including corners) should she look for?

Also, Sandy's uncle has already bought next year's jigsaw, which has 204 edge pieces (including corners). How many total pieces does next year's puzzle have?

Answer on page 274.

HAVE A HEART

All 13 hearts from a standard deck of cards are arranged here. Which one is face down?

Answer on page 268.

TAKE AIM

In a dart game of 201, players must throw exactly 201 points to win. They count backward, and must throw a double with their last dart.

All wedges count their face value. The small outer ring counts double and the small inner ring counts triple (the dart shows 3 × 7, or 21). The inner circle is 25 points and the bull's-eye is a double 25, or 50 points.

With three darts, it is possible to go out with as many as 170 points left. How? And how would you go out if you had 164 points? 149 points?

Answers on page 278.

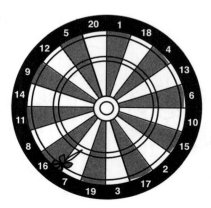

MAKING FACES

At an unusual costume party, every guest is wearing a mask showing the face of another one of the guests. The nametags match the masks. Can you name all of the people under the false faces?

Answer on page 270.

GO FOR A SPIN

In each case, can you mentally rotate the wheels so that six three-letter words are spelled from the outside ring to the center? Hint: All of the words in each grid have something in common.

Answers on page 266.

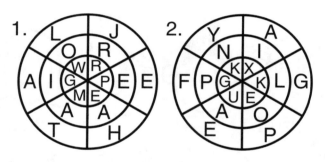

WHAT'S THE BUZZ?

Locusts are a type of grasshopper that can travel in swarms of billions of insects and destroy crops. If one variety of plague locust appears every seven years and another variety appears every 12 years, and both types of locust hatched in the same year in 1957, when did (or when will) both varieties appear again in the same year? Also, in what year before 1957 did both types appear?

Answer on page 280.

PRETZEL LOGIC

Which of the pretzel pieces below comes from a bag of Mrs. Saline pretzels and which ones must have come from a different brand?

Answer on page 274.

Mrs. Saline Pretzel:

SNACK ATTACK

Sally and Julie put their change together (shown below) and want to buy some snacks from the vending machines in their hotel. What can they afford to buy if they want to get two of each item?

- SODA: 65¢
- CHIPS: 80¢
- CANDY BAR: 50¢
- GUM: 45¢

Answer on page 276.

CONCENTRATION

There are eight pairs of cards ranked two through nine in this game of Concentration. Given the hints shown below and the two cards that are overturned, can you figure out where all of the pairs are?

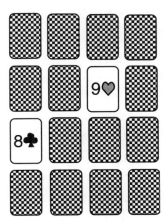

1. No pairs appear in the same row or column.

2. No pairs appear in the same long diagonal.

3. The fourth column has only even numbers.

4. The second column has only odd numbers.

5. The first row contains the numbers 2 to 5.

6. The second row contains the numbers 6 to 9.

7. The corners contain the numbers 2 to 5.

8. There is a 3 in the upper left corner and a 4 in the lower right corner.

Answer on page 262.

A WHALE'S TALE

Starting at the I in the upper left-hand corner, can you make knight's moves (see below) to jump to every square in the grid, without landing in any square twice, so that the letters you visit, in order, spell a phrase that tells you something about a blue whale's heart?

Answer on page 280.

I	N	E	S	B
T	P	T	I	N
U	N	E	E	E
E	I	T	I	M
S	T	R	M	A

Knightís move

1		
		2

ORCHESTRATION

In the Pinedale Orchestra, there are 14 violinists and 8 cellists. Of those orchestra members, 5 belong to the Fencing Club and half are in the Snake Lovers Association. Of the 14 orchestra members in the clubs, only 2 belong to both, neither of whom are cellists. If 6 violinists are in neither club and 3 cellists are in the snake group, how many violinists are fencers? And how many cellists belong to neither club?

Answer on page 272.

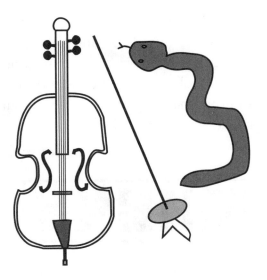

MILEAGE MILESTONES

Jean likes to take note of three mileage milestones on her odometer:

- Every time four of the same digits appear consecutively
- Every time the five-digit mileage is a palindrome (reads the same forward and backward)
- Every time the mileage is a "full house"; that is, two of one digit and three of another in any nonpalindromic order

One day, Jean noticed one milestone, noticed a second milestone 45 miles later, and a third milestone five miles after that. She noticed the third milestone again in one mile, followed by the second milestone in five miles and the first again in 45 miles. What were the mileage readings at each of those times?

Answer on page 270.

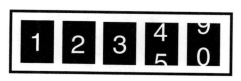

GRILL SERGEANT

Joe is in charge of buying the food for his company picnic. Joe's butcher sells hot dogs in packages of 12. At the store, buns come in packages of eight and paper plates are sold in multiples of 25. If Joe wants to use everything that he buys, with no leftovers, what is the fewest number of hot dogs that he has to grill?

Answer on page 267.

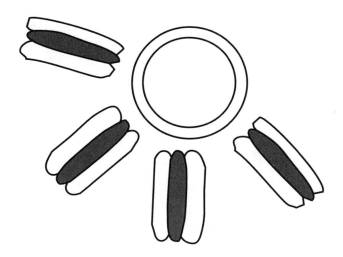

CALENDAR GIRLS

Lydia and her friends are trying to find a good time for the next meeting of their investment club. Looking at next month, and the obligations that the five women already have, which weekday evening (or evenings) are possible meeting times?

- Lydia has volleyball games on Tuesdays and Thursdays.

S	M	T	W	T	F	S
			1	2	3	4
5	6	7	8	9	10	11
12	13	14	15	16	17	18
19	20	21	22	23	24	25
26	27	28	29	30	31	

- Sophie volunteers with Meals on Wheels every third day starting on the first.

- Daisy is busy every other Friday starting the 3rd and has tickets to concerts on the 15th and 29th.

- Fiona can't meet on Mondays and has book club on the eighth.

Answer on page 261.

PUNCTUALITY

Can you add punctuation to make each of the following statements true?

1) she said two hundred and twenty is the product of two and ten and eleven is five plus six and also seven plus four

2) he jumped fifty times three is one hundred fifty over fifty four equals ninety less eighty six hundred is not a verb

Answer on page 274.

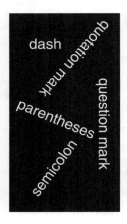

ATTENTION, SHOPPERS

Lusina spent exactly $29 at a garage sale. If only the items shown were for sale, and she paid the prices as they are marked, what did she buy?

Answer on page 260.

ATLAS $3

HAT $11

PICTURE $4

LAMP $7

MAILBOX $5

IRON $8

THE RIGHT DIRECTION

Ray and Wendy were driving to a surprise party. Ray knew what part of town they were going to, but he couldn't find the house. They passed Owl Street and it started raining. By the time they drove by Rabbit Court for the third time, it was getting close to 12:00, when the guest was to arrive. Ray asked to see the scrap of

paper that the address was written on.

"Aha," he said, "Now I know what the problem is."

Do you?

Answer on page 275.

NUMBER LINES

Can you draw the straight line that passes through the highest number total for each box below?

Answer on page 272.

A

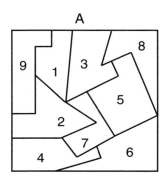

B

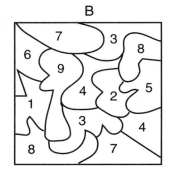

READY TO ROLL

One of the dice below is not a standard die. Which one is the fake?

Answer on page 274.

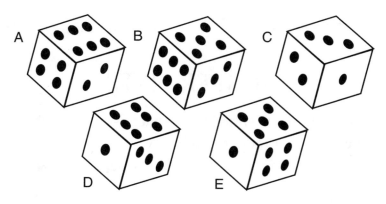

MUDDLED

Each clue on the following page can be answered with a five-letter word. In all, those words use only 10 letters. One 10-letter word can be spelled using all those letters. Can you find it?

1. Be uncertain about
2. Make less blurry
3. Performed in a play
4. Sailing vessels
5. Huge meal
6. Chopped into dice-like pieces

Answer on page 271.

ORDER, PLEASE

Ms. Carter, the homeroom teacher, lined up six students in the order shown by A. Not satisfied, she rearranged them in the order shown by B. What is the basis for each sequence?

Answer on page 272.

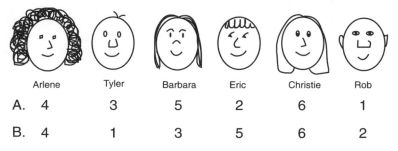

	Arlene	Tyler	Barbara	Eric	Christie	Rob
A.	4	3	5	2	6	1
B.	4	1	3	5	6	2

GUESSTIMATION

Guess the number that correctly completes each statement below.

1. There are __ ridges on a quarter.
2. There are __ ridges on a dime.
3. You can fold a sheet of newspaper in half __ times.
4. There are ___ dimples on a golf ball.
5. There are __ letters in the Hawaiian alphabet.
6. You have to lick __ stamps to consume one calorie.
7. The average polar bear lives __ years.

a. 8   b. 10   c. 12   d. 20   e. 118   f. 119   g. 336

Answers on page 267.

CROSS WORDS

The words listed below fit into a grid so that each letter in the grid is used in one word reading across and one word reading down. Can you figure out the shape of the grid and how the words fit together?

Answer on page 263.

ALONE	GENIE
ATONE	MANIA
DAM	SAG
DATES	SALAD
DEE	SEA

LED ASTRAY

The LED display on Art's calculator is malfunctioning. Only the top halves of the characters are showing. What equation is displayed below?

If only the bottom halves of the display are showing, what are the two possibilities for the equation?

Answer on page 269.

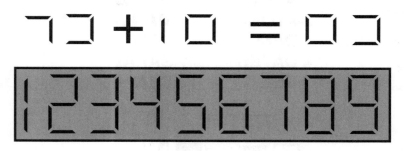

WHOA, BABY!

Jen gave birth to her daughter Caroline on the first of January in a year following a leap year. Starting in February, on the first of the month throughout that year, she made note of the day of the week. She noticed that the monthly anniversary of her daughter's birth fell

on a Friday three times that year.
On what day of the week was
Caroline born? And how
many months old was
Caroline before her monthly
"birthday" fell on its original day for the
third time (not counting her actual day of birth)?

Answer on page 280.

STICK HOUSES

In case A, can you move one stick and add another to create two matching houses? Case B shows a farmer's pigpen. Can you move two fences and add two more to create two pigpens of the same shape and size?

Answer on page 277.

A.

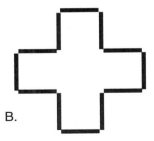

B.

CIRCULAR NOTIONS

The circles below are hiding two interesting words. To find the words, start at the top letter in each case, and count clockwise a number of spaces (the number is for you to determine) to the next letter. Then, keep counting the same number of spaces and landing on a new letter until all the letters are used.

Answer on page 262.

1.
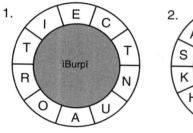

2.
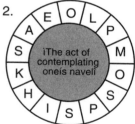

LETTER CODES

The code below hides two nonsense sentences. Only the 10 most common letters in English are used in the codes. The most common letter appears 10 times, the next most common appears nine times, etc. What are the two sentences and what are the 10 most frequently used letters in English?

1. Q UWGZW G BWGU GBUWGUWX QB GZQG.

2. ZWW, QU'Z UPP JPU UP JPPU QB WXQW
   —JWGK PB.

ABCDEFGHIJKLMNOPQRSTUVWXYZ

Answer on page 269.

REBUS RIDDLES

Add and subtract the letters of the illustrated words as indicated to find the answers to the riddles.

Answer on page 275.

1. What has a head but no eyes?

2. What has an eye but no head?

ANSWERS

Ages of Reason

Aunt Pearl is 64 years old (LXIV) and her daughter is 46 (XLVI). The numbers 66 (LXVI) and 44 (XLIV) can also be made from the same symbols.

Alligator Ally

The alligator is on the left and is lying.

Animal Strength

The frogs will win the third tug of war. Two turtles will tie with four frogs.

Attention, Shoppers

Lusina bought the atlas, hat, lamp, and iron.

Beady Eyes

8,888 was added to abacus A (8,375) to get the sum on abacus B (17,263).

Berry Impressive

There will be 34 strawberries at the beginning of November. The number of berries each month is the famous Fibonacci sequence (1, 1, 2, 3, 5, 8, ...), where each number is the sum of the previous two.

Black and White

1. You have two white cards.
2. You have one white card and one black card. (If you had two black cards, A would know what he had on the second round, because if he had two of the same card, one of you would have seen four of one color and known you had two of the other color.)

Blind Alleys

They started in Redland.

Block Party

She took the "CUBE ROUTE."

Calendar Girls

The only day that works for everyone is Friday the 24th.

Catch a Code

HE FELT REMORSE (re"Morse.")

Categorically Speaking

	S	**C**	**A**	**M**	**P**
Girls' names:	Scarlet	Candy	Amber	Myrtle	Pearl
Colors:	sand	coral	amethyst	magenta	purple
Trees:	spruce	chestnut	apple	mango	palm
Flowers:	snowball	camellia	amaryllis	magnolia	primrose
On a beach:	shell	chair	anemone	mussel	pail

Circular Notions

1. ERUCTATION (count 7 squares at a time)
2. OMPHALOSKEPSIS (count 3 squares at a time)

Coffee Break

A cup of tea has one-half the caffeine of a cup of coffee, and two times the caffeine of a can of cola.

Concentration

Cross Words

Detective Story

Slooth should arrest the man in the Civic. Chiller is calling from Thunder Bay, Ontario, where they measure the temperature in Celsius. Thirty degrees Celsius is 86 degrees Fahrenheit.

Domino Effect

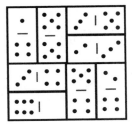

Rotations of this arrangement also work.

Draw by Numbers

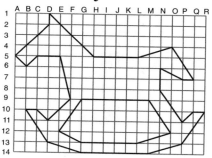

Familiar Faces

All of the coins are correct except for the dime.

Fishing for Words

The proverb reads, "The fish dies because he opens his mouth."

Fishing Lines

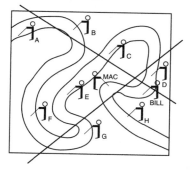

Fit for a Princess

The princess can wear four combinations of one piece of jewelry, six combinations of two, four combinations of three, and one combination of all four jewels, for a total of 15 different combinations.

Fit to Be Tiled

The 8 × 8 table can be covered with shape B (but not shape A). The 8 × 6 table can be covered with shape A (but not shape B).

For Your Thoughts

1. A   2. C

Fraction Words

A. Florida (fl + or + ida)   B. piano (pi + an + o)

Game Plan

A: Player X wins; B: Player X wins (X plays above O first, then no matter where O plays, X can either win on the next turn or take the lowest empty right-hand box and win on the following turn).

Get the Scoop

The free ice cream will be on the first Tuesday in July.

Give Me Five

These are our answers (there may be others):

$(3 \times 3 + 3 + 3) \div 3 = 5$

$(4 - 4 + 4) \div 4 + 4 = 5$

$5 - 5 + 5 - 5 + 5 = 5$

$6 - (6 \div 6) + (6 - 6) = 5$

$7 - (7 \div 7) - (7 \div 7) = 5$

$8 - [(8 + 8 + 8) \div 8] = 5$

$[(9 \times 9) + 9] \div (9 + 9) = 5$

Global Economy

The best deal is in Sweden, where the CD costs an equivalent of $9 U.S.

Go for a Spin

1: jaw, ear, hip, toe, arm, and leg.

2: ape, gnu, pig, elk, fox, and yak.

A Good Egg

1. T; 2. W; 3. E; 4. L; 5. V; 6. E. An ostrich egg equals about 24 hen's eggs, or 12 omelets.

Got Class?

This class schedule will work: Biology, European history, Genetics, Shakespeare, and Statistics.

Graphic Language

Because seven eight nine ("seven ate nine").

The Great Pumpkin

Tom has enough of everything except eggs. He will need one more egg to make two pies.

Grill Sergeant

To use everything that he buys, Joe must grill at least 600 hot dogs (50 packages of dogs, 75 packages of buns, and 24 packages of plates). Any multiple of 600 will also come out even.

Guesstimation

1-f; 2-e; 3-a; 4-g; 5-c; 6-b; 7-d.

Hairy Tales

1. Rapunzel was trapped for 200 years.
2. Rip Van Winkle's beard should have been 10 feet long.

Have a Heart

The 10 of hearts is face down.

Hula Hoopla

The equations represent these numbers: 1. $2 \times 2 + 5 = 9$; 2. $8 \div 4 \times 2 = 4$; 3. $9 \div 3 + 3 = 6$; 4. $2 + 6 - 3 = 5$ or e'lima.

Irish Eyes

It's About Time

1. B (7–11); 2. D (9 to 5); 3. E (737); 4. A (1040); 5. C (5' 10"); 6. F (101).

Jollos and Plotz

Jollos have a circle, triangle, and two lines; plotz have a circle and four lines. A and C are plotz.

Jumper Cables

Stan and Jan are grabbing the same rope.

Keep the Faith

Old Faithful's next eruption will be at 4:50 P.M. The formula used to figure out the time until the next eruption is 4D + 30 minutes, where D is the duration of the last eruption.

Key Rings

A. yes

B. no (two groups of two are connected)

C. yes

LED Astray

Top portion showing: 73 + 19 = 92.

Lower portion showing: 45 + 18 = 63 or 49 + 16 = 65.

Letter Codes

1. I tease a neat anteater in Asia.

2. See, it's too hot to hoot in Erie—head on.

The 10 most common letters, in order of use, are: e, t, a, o, i, n, s, h, r, and d.

Losing Track

Deb cheated. The answers are: 1. bison; 2. caribou; 3. deer; 4. moose; 5. mountain goat.

Making Faces

From left to right from the top: Max, Maude, Wade, Walt, Vance, Mona, Mimi, and Boris.

Match Boxes

Only piece e will not form a box.

Math Maze

BEGIN

$3	+4	ñ1	•4	˜5
•2	ñ5	•3	-8	ñ2
•0	•7	˜2	+6	˜3
˜5	•6	+1	•5	+2
+8	˜4	+7	ñ9	=9

END

Mileage Milestones

49,949; 49,994; 49,999; 50,000; 50,005; and 50,050.

Mind Boggler

The numbers ONE through TEN can be spelled by moving from letter to adjacent letter. THREE is the only number that cannot be spelled (without using the same E two times in a row).

Mirror Images

Figures four and seven are impossible with just one mirror.

Muddled

1. doubt; 2. focus; 3. acted; 4. boats; 5. feast; 6. cubed. The 10-letter word is OBFUSCATED.

Next in Line

Each item is spelled with all the letters from the one before, plus one: TEA, TAPE, PLEAT, and STAPLE. The next item in the sequence is PLANETS (a).

Novel Idea

1. AUTHRSAREALL
2. AWHRSAREALL
3. AWHRSAREALLDD
4. AWHRSARETHEALLDD

5. AWHRSARETHEALNLDND
6. AWHRSIATRETHEALNLDND
7. AWHRSIATRETHEALNLDMEND
8. WRITEHANDED
9. WRITE HANDED

Number Lines

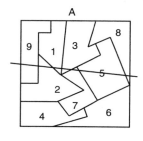 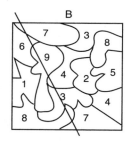

A. 35; B. 44.

Orchestration

Two violinists are fencers (they are also in the snake club). Two cellists are in neither group.

Order, Please

In the first case, the kids are in order of the length of their first names; in the second, the names form a chain in which the last letter of each name is the first letter of the next.

Out of Shape

B, F, G, and I are not versions of the original shape.

Paper Clip Flip

Number 1 is shorter than the original. Numbers 3 and 10 are longer than the original.

Paper Pinball

10, +20, −5, +10, +15, +5, +10, −10, +15, +10, +5, +40, −20, +25, +40, −5, +10, −10, +25, +5, +15, −5, +30, −10, +15, +30, +20, + 5 = 295.

The Penny Fairy

Four miles of pennies equals $3,379.20; one ton equals $3,657.14. The ton is $277.94 more.

Pieces of Wisdom

"To laugh often and much."

Pie-Eyed

Here's one answer: Put five cherries in one bowl, five cherries in another, and put one of those inside the third bowl, which holds two cherries.

Pretzel Logic

Pieces two and eight are not Mrs. Saline pretzels.

Produce Products

The equations are: $9 - 3 = 6$; $4 \times 2 = 8$; $1 + 4 = 5$; and $6 \div 3 = 2$. Therefore, the carrot is 7.

Punctuality

1) She said, "two hundred." And twenty is the product of two and ten. And eleven is five plus six and also seven plus four.
2) He jumped fifty times. Three is one hundred fifty over fifty. Four equals ninety less eighty-six. "Hundred" is not a verb.

Puzzle Puzzle

This year's puzzle has 176 edge pieces (45 per side—the corner pieces are part of two sides). Next year's puzzle has 2,704 total pieces.

Ready to Roll

Die D is not a standard die (all pairs of numbers on opposite sides should add up to seven).

Rebus Riddles

1. bead + rug + stem − bag − tees = drum
2. stork + nail + radio − ski − rail = tornado

Receipt Deceit

Hank's purchases were 3.25 + 0.75 + 1.30 = 5.30 + .25 tax = $5.55. The sale before his was for 1.80 + 4.96 + 0.64 = 7.40 + .35 tax = $7.75.

The Right Direction

Wendy was looking at the scrap of paper upside down. They should have been looking for 819 Pooh. Ray recognized that Owl Street and Rabbit Court were part of the same *Winnie-the-Pooh* themed neighborhood.

Ruff and Ready

There were 28 people and 35 dogs.

Runed Punch Line

What did the chickens get when they crossed the freeway? Cheep thrills.

Sea or Soil?

The treasure is buried under water.

Secret Words

The first word is CROW; the second word is RAVEN.

Self Test

1. 8; 2. 6; 3. 4; 4. 1; 5. 9; 6. 7; 7. 5; 8. 3; 9. 2.

Shifting Gears

1. clockwise; 2. clockwise; 3. counterclockwise; 4. these gears won't turn.

Slice of Life

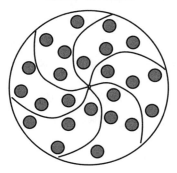

Snack Attack

The girls have $2.30. They can buy two sodas and two candy bars.

Starry Eyes

Stick Houses

A.

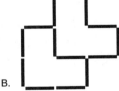

B.

Strike It, Rich

Rich had 11 strikes in a row, but threw a gutter ball on the last ball of the 10th frame for 290 points in 110 pins. Carl hit 110 pins by throwing a gutter ball followed by a spare (all 10 pins) in the first 10 frames and a strike on the bonus ball of the 10th frame, for a total of 110 points—a difference of 180 points.

Symbol Maze

Starting with the circle: A1, A3, C2, A2, D3, B1, D1, B2, D2, B3, C1, and C3.

Take Aim

Triple 20, triple 20, bull's-eye = 170. Triple 19, triple 19, bull's-eye = 164. Triple 20, triple 19, double 16 = 149. (Other possibilities exist for 164 and 149.)

Talk for a Spell

a-florist (FLOWERS); b-health club (WORKOUT); c-barber (HAIRCUT); d-travel agent (FLY AWAY); e-coffee shop (HOT JAVA); f-costume shop (DRESS UP); g-veterinarian (PET CARE); h-bank (SAVE NOW).

Technique-Color

Piece A should be orange.

Ten Gold Coins

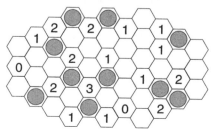

Theory of Relativity

You are Bernie.

Thirteen Candles

The candles form 50 triangles: 18 made by the six points around the edge; 18 using the full side of the two large triangles; 12 made of half of a full side; and 2 large triangles.

Three Hexes

Numbers three and seven are made with four hexagons.

To the Letter

In order, the letters spell "verbatim."

Tough Cookies

There were 36 cookies on the plate.

12-Step Program

The output reads: BOOT UP.

Tying the Knot

She should start her subscription to *Brides* magazine. Ropes 1, 2, and 5 will form knots.

Unfolding Mystery

1 matches a and 2 matches f.

A Whale's Tale

The phrase is: It beats nine times per minute.

What's the Buzz?

The two varieties of locusts appear together every 84 years: 1873, 1957, and 2041.

What's the Plan?

Object one fits the plan.

Whoa, Baby!

Caroline was born on a Tuesday. She was 18 months old when her "birthday" fell on a Tuesday for the third time (in her second July).

Winter Eyes

A–1; B–7; C–4.

Zoned Out

Assuming her plane is on time, Amy will arrive at Kennedy airport at 7 a.m. on Friday.

INDEX

Santana

Santana

WHAT IS MENSA?

Mensa—The High IQ Society

Mensa is the international society for people with a high IQ. We have more than 100,000 members in over 40 countries worldwide.

The society's aims are:
- to identify and foster human intelligence for the benefit of humanity;
- to encourage research in the nature, characteristics, and uses of intelligence;
- to provide a stimulating intellectual and social environment for its members.

Anyone with an IQ score in the top two percent of the population is eligible to become a member of Mensa—are you the "one in 50" we've been looking for?

Mensa membership offers an excellent range of benefits:
- Networking and social activities nationally and around the world;
- Special Interest Groups (hundreds of chances to pursue your hobbies and interests—from art to zoology!);
- Monthly International Journal, national magazines, and regional newsletters;
- Local meetings—from game challenges to food and drink;
- National and international weekend gatherings and conferences;
- Intellectually stimulating lectures and seminars;
- Access to the worldwide SIGHT network for travelers and hosts.

**For more information about
Mensa International:**

www.mensa.org
Mensa International
15 The Ivories
6–8 Northampton Street
Islington, London N1 2HY
United Kingdom

**For more information about
American Mensa:**

www.us.mensa.org
Telephone: (800) 66-MENSA
American Mensa Ltd.
1229 Corporate Drive West
Arlington, TX 76006-6103 US

**For more information about
British Mensa (UK and Ireland):**

www.mensa.org.uk
Telephone: +44 (0) 1902 772771
E-mail: enquiries@mensa.org.uk
British Mensa Ltd.
St. John's House
St. John's Square
Wolverhampton WV2 4AH
United Kingdom